PHalarope Books

PHalarope Books are designed specifically for the amateur naturalist. These volumes represent excellence in natural history publishing. Most books in the PHalarope series are based on a nature course or program at the college or adult education level or are sponsored by a museum or nature center. Each PHalarope book reflects the author's teaching ability as well as writing ability. Among the books:

BOOKS IN SERIES

The Amateur Naturalist's Handbook
Vinson Brown

Botany in the Field: An Introduction to Plant Communities for the Amateur Naturalist
Jane Scott

The Curious Naturalist
John Mitchell and the Massachusetts Audubon Society

Discover the Invisible: A Naturalist's Guide to Using the Microscope
Eric V. Gravé

A Field Guide to the Familiar: Learning to Observe The Natural World
Gale Lawrence

Insect Life: A Field Entomology Manual for the Amateur Naturalist
Ross H. Arnett, Jr. and Richard L. Jacques, Jr.

Nature Drawing: A Tool for Learning
Clare Walker Leslie

The Plant Observer's Guidebook: A Field Botany Manual for the Amateur Naturalist
Charles E. Roth

Pond and Brook: A Guide to Nature Study in Freshwater Environments
Michael J. Caduto

The Sky Observer's Guidebook
Charles E. Roth

Suburban Wildflowers: An Introduction to the Common Wildflowers of Your Back Yard and Local Park
Richard Headstrom

Suburban Wildlife: An Introduction to the Common Animals of Your Back Yard and Local Park
Richard Headstrom

Thoreau's Method: A Handbook for Nature Study
David Pepi

The Wildlife Observer's Guidebook
Charles E. Roth, Massachusetts Audubon Society

Butterflies and Moths: A Companion to Your Field Guide
Jo Brewer and Dave Winter

Butterflies
and
Moths

A Companion to
Your Field Guide

Jo Brewer and Dave Winter

DRAWINGS BY *Channing Thieme*
PHOTOGRAPHS BY *Jo Brewer and Dave Winter*

PHalarope
Books / **PRENTICE HALL PRESS • NEW YORK**

Published by Prentice Hall Press
A Division of Simon & Schuster, Inc.
Gulf+Western Building
One Gulf+Western Plaza
New York, NY   10023

PRENTICE HALL PRESS is a trademark of Simon & Schuster, Inc.

Library of Congress Cataloging-in-Publication Data

Brewer, Jo.
  Butterflies and moths.

  (PHalarope books)
  Bibliograph: p.
  Includes index.
  1. Lepidoptera.   I. Winter, Dave.   II. Title.
QL544.B74   1986   595.78   86-3182

ISBN 0-13-108846-7

Designed by Irving Perkins Associates

Manufactured in the United States of America

10 9 8 7 6 5 4 3 2 1

First Edition

This book is dedicated
to
Tom, Jeff, and Leeds,
whose childhood curiosity kindled the fire,
and to
the late Clarence S. Dike,
who planted the seed that refused to stop growing.

Acknowledgments·

In addition to the many amateur and professional lepidopterists around the country who, both before and during the preparation of this book, have shared with us their knowledge and experience, we should particularly like to thank the following: Deane Bowers and Frank M. Carpenter, Harvard University; Francie Chew, Tufts University; Charles C. Covell, Jr., University of Louisville; Larry Gall, Yale University; Paul Opler, Office of Endangered Species; Dale Schweitzer, The Nature Conservancy; and Carroll M. Williams, Harvard University. The assistance of Jeff Brewer, who did our photographic processing, was indispensable. Our appreciation is extended to Mary Kennan, editor; John Talbot, editorial assistant; Laurie S. Barnett, managing editor; and Tracy Behar, production editor, for their roles in the creation of this book.

Contents·

PART III   On the Matter of Names

PART IV   To Collect or Not to Collect?

PART V Tricks and Tools

The color insert follows page 114.

Preface·

There have been several good books written for the identification of moths and numerous volumes for the identification of butterflies.

This book, in contrast, is written to introduce the reader to the enjoyment of moths and butterflies by observing them, by rearing them through their immature stages from egg to adult, and, for those who may be so inclined, by collecting and preserving specimens. It will seek to help the interested observer to understand the nature of these fascinating and varied insects, their developmental stages, and their habits and habitats, as well as the hazards they face in each stage of growth and their varied ways of coping with these hazards. This understanding, in turn, can make it possible to find and observe moths and butterflies in places easily overlooked, increasing the excitement and fascination of the pursuit.

There are those who collect these insects as one may collect postage stamps, by purchasing them from catalogs. There are those whose interest is in the use of insects, or parts of them, in the production of artifacts. This book is not for them.

Those who become "hooked" on moths and butterflies (lepidoptera) reap satisfactions perhaps unanticipated—the pleasures of discoveries in the out-of-doors, whether weed lot or wilderness; vacations made exciting and unique, away from the expensive and contrived "attractions" of the travel brochures; the camaraderie of visiting and exploring with other lepidopterists, a most hospitable group, whether professional or amateur; the satisfaction and economy of creating one's own gadgets and equipment; and the occasional reward of a real scientific contribution, either by chance observation or through diligent study.

We, the authors, are not professional entomologists, although we have spent much time with those who are. What we have gleaned over many decades from them, from other interested amateurs, and from the moths and butterflies themselves, forms the basis of this book.

The greatest satisfaction of this pursuit has been the sharing of our interest and enthusiasm with others, particularly with children, to help open their eyes to this world that the insects have been forced to share with us.

PART I

People
and Lepidoptera

CHAPTER 1

What Are Moths and Butterflies?

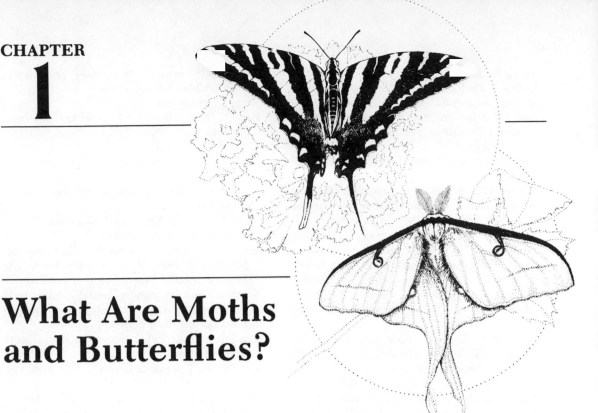

Figure 1–1 Zebra swallowtail (*Eurytides marcellus*) and luna moth (*Actias luna*)

Whenever people start to think about moths and butterflies, two questions seem to come immediately to the fore. "What are moths and butterflies (that is, what distinguishes them from other insects)?" And "How can one tell a butterfly from a moth?" A dialogue might go something like this:

NOVICE: Butterflies wear cloaks of many colors! Wings that dart crookedly over the summer meadows, pausing here and there among flowers and then disappearing, perhaps never to be seen again, but in that one moment so graceful, so silent, so briefly a thing of magic!

PROFESSIONAL: ...and moths?

NOV.: Oh, moths are small, winged blurs in the headlights of our automobiles. They're brown, and they bump against window screens at night. They're small, drab trian-

gles perched on the wall near our porch lights. Everyone knows that moths are the things that chew up our woolens in the summer while we are away on vacation!

PRO.: All moths?

NOV.: Maybe not all, but a lot of them do.

PRO.: That is the difference then? That moths chew your clothes, and butterflies do not?

NOV.: Partly, at least. I guess.

PRO.: Partly? Then what is a moth, and what is a butterfly? Linnaeus, the famous Swedish naturalist who first classified the animals, called all the butterflies and moths Lepidoptera.

NOV.: Why?

PRO.: Because *lepis* is the Greek word for scale, and *pteron* the word for wing. Moths and butterflies are the only insects that have wings clothed with scales.

NOV.: Just as I thought. A butterfly's wings are colorful, and a moth's wings are dingy.

PRO.: They both have scales on their wings,

and a head with antennae, compound eyes, and a coiled tongue called a proboscis, a thorax bearing six long legs and four wings, and an abdomen; they both have the same system of breathing, circulating blood, and digesting food.

NOV.: But the moths have dingy wings. Right?

PRO.: That premise is incorrect. Some of the night-flying moths you mentioned in connection with the headlights and porch lights are indeed quite drab and dingy, but the tiger moths and underwing moths that fly in the night are quite spectacular in their colors. Other night fliers have wings with patterns of utmost delicacy that, in the minds of many people, outclass the boldness of design for which butterflies are noted.

NOV.: If they only fly at night, how does a person know if they are colorful or not?

PRO.: Well, there are the hummingbird sphinx moths. They fly by day. And don't forget those handsome black and white buck moths that fly around by day, showing off their red "tail feathers" and looking for females.

NOV.: What I was really hoping to learn was how to go out into the field and be able to tell whether I was seeing butterflies or moths.

PRO.: All attempts to find an absolutely foolproof way to tell moths from butterflies are doomed to failure, because there are always exceptions.

NOV.: So, after all else is sifted away, we are left with the following information: that all butterflies and moths have a proboscis, scales on their wings, six walking legs, and they don't make any noise.

PRO.: Well, actually all butterflies have probosces. Most moths also have probosces, but the silk moths are different. Not only do they lack probosces, they have no mouth parts at all. They do all their eating while they are caterpillars, and when they become adults they have to live on stored food.

NOV.: Silk moths can't eat.... So now we know that all butterflies and moths have scales on their wings, they have six walking legs, and they don't make any noise.

PRO.: Well, actually butterflies and moths have scales on their wings...

NOV.: ...and some are colorful...

PRO.: ...but that doesn't mean that all lepidoptera have scales on their wings.

NOV.: But you said...?

PRO.: In the American tropics there are many butterflies, both big and small, that have almost no scales on their wings. You can see right through them!

NOV.: No scales? So now all they have in common is six legs and no noise!

PRO.: Well, there is a slight difference between the legs of some butterflies. The brush-footed butterflies (nymphalids), satyrs, and monarchs actually have only four walking legs. The other two are just held against their bodies.

NOV.: Is that a useful clue to telling a moth from a butterfly?

PRO.: Well, I suppose if you caught one with only four legs it couldn't be a moth.

NOV.: I hope I can remember that. And at least, if I hear a noise it will probably be a cricket.

PRO.: I realize that this is not helping you to put all butterflies in one box and all moths in another, but I think you might like to know that not all butterflies are totally silent, and neither are all moths. They cannot chirp, to be sure, but sometimes thay can make themselves heard. Take the zebra swallowtail, for example. When it emerges from its chrysalis, it comes out with a cracking sound loud enough to be heard six feet away. Then there are the tropical butterflies of the genus *Hamadryas*. When they fly they make a loud clicking sound with every wing beat. And the Old World death's head sphinx moth, when disturbed, makes a sound like a squeaking mouse.

NOV.: Is this a useful clue or just another complication?

PRO.: Well, when talking about lepidoptera, no generalization is really safe, but there does seem to be one reliable difference, which relates to the antennae.

NOV.: At last! And what is that?

PRO.: Well, you see, there are two groups of butterflies, the true butterflies and the skippers. Some skippers tend to look more like moths than like butterflies, because their bodies are large compared to their wings, which are small, often brown and tawny...

NOV.: Not colorful?

PRO.: ...and held in an unusual position. That is, the hind wings are held flat, but the forewings are held half open when they are resting. Other skippers are more like butterflies than moths, since their wings are colorful and rather large. These types hold their wings open while resting, as most butterflies do. One such species, the mangrove skipper found in Florida, is black with iridescent blue hind wings and is larger than a painted lady. Another is partly iridescent green with long tails, and about the size of a sulphur butterfly.

NOV.: It sounds like a swallowtail to me.

PRO.: Both rest with wide open wings. All this would be confusing to me, too, were it not for one little detail.

NOV.: And what, pray tell, is that?

PRO.: It is that all lepidoptera have antennae.

NOV.: All?

PRO.: Yes. But they are not all the same.

NOV.: I'm not surprised.

PRO.: The antennae of moths are either hairlike, saw-toothed, or plumed, and in these designs the moths are unique. No other lepidoptera have hairlike, saw-toothed, or plumed antennae.

NOV.: I am amazed.

PRO.: The antennae of butterflies are smooth, with knobs at the ends.

NOV.: Knobs at the ends?

PRO.: Yes.

NOV.: All butterflies have antennae that are knobbed at the ends. All moths have antennae that are hairlike, saw-toothed, or plumed.

PRO.: That is correct, all except for one little minor detail.

NOV.: Yes?

PRO.: Skippers have knobbed antennae, but the end is drawn out into a hairlike point or a hook.

NOV.: At last! Now I can tell a moth from a butterfly.

CHAPTER
2

The Lure of Moths and Butterflies

Figure 2–1 All eyes on woolly bear

Did you ever stop to examine the wing of a butterfly? I don't mean killing the butterfly to find out what it is made of. I mean a butterfly someone may have given you, or one found on the road—a road-kill butterfly. Have you ever taken a reading glass, or better still, a microscope, to help you see how the wing patterns are put together? Have you ever noticed the shapes of different scales in different parts of the wings? Have you ever noticed that on the wings of some butterflies there are "eyespots" that look like the eyes of small snakes? Have you ever thought what a monumental task it would be to reproduce the pattern on the underside of the wing of an American painted lady (*Vanessa virginiensis*), which flaunts a brilliantly pupilled eye? And did you notice that around the "eye" there is a snarl of straw-colored lines— the color of dry grass?

Have you ever seen a moth laying eggs on a leaf or a twig, eggs you might confiscate and rear? Eggs you might watch until the small caterpillars chew their way to freedom?

How often have you walked a wooded road at night with only a flashlight to guide you? And did the flashlight reveal a scene of revelry below the stub of a broken branch, as varied moths, from small, drab sallows to the great black witch, feasted on oozing sap?

You have seen butterflies and moths from time to time, but did you notice the shapes of their wings. Were they pointed? Rounded? Notched? Tailed? Have you seen wings with transparent windows? Have you watched the drama of instant change when drab brown underwing moths, hidden on weathered bark, open with a flash of color and vanish among trees?

Have you stayed long enough to watch a mass of small newborn caterpillars jockeying for position on one tree, or on one leaf? Some such lively little congregations may be drab, unmarked, all but naked—others, like "Solomon in all his glory," garbed in ermine, velvet, chenille, or adorned with tufts, plumes, bristles, spines, horns.... Some have false "eyes," others have glands called "osmeteria" that, when extruded, resemble the tongues of snakes.

Have you seen a caterpillar shed its skin for the last time, remaining afterward as a strange little "blob," silently squirming and twisting and later forming its own unique shape and colors: the pupa of a moth, shiny mahogany, blimp-shaped, and slippery to the touch, or the chrysalis of the butterfly, jade, pure gold, the green of new leaves, the brown of old ones? Days and months go by: the pupa or the chrysalis splits, in its own time, in accord with events preordained. Antennae, proboscis, and legs push their way into daylight, beneath the burden of wings still limp and crumpled. And finding some sun-warmed spot, the new butterfly or moth stops and waits and spreads its wings to dry.

We, as humans, experience a slowly widening path from birth to knowledge. The life of a lepidopteran is a series of seemingly unrelated changes, called metamorphoses, by which one form is concealed within the next until the climax is revealed. The cycle from egg to caterpillar to chrysalis to imago is en-

hanced by the differences that accompany each new larval stage. Some caterpillars, like those of the pipe vine swallowtail (*Battus philenor*), become larger images of their former selves with each moult. Others, like the tiger swallowtail (*Papilio glaucus*), change color and pattern with each stage.

The caterpillars of the silk moths and the large sphinx moths become increasingly bizarre in color and design, and awesomely large. The hickory horned devil (which becomes the royal walnut moth, *Citheronia regalis*) grows to a length of 5½" and bears an array of horns that evoke the image of a legendary dragon. The tomato hornworm (tomato sphinx moth, *Manduca quinquemaculata*) justifies its name by raising its head to the position and dignity of an Egyptian sphinx.

Walking, loafing in the sun, and exploring new places are always delightful, but with moths and butterflies in mind a new dimension is added. Every field, roadside, stream, beach, wood, or hilltop has its resident butterflies. There are no tickets to buy, no dues to pay. One of our amateur lepidopterist friends, who systematically visited all the parks and cemeteries within New York City, has found over seventy species of butterflies, well over half the number known to occur in the rural areas beyond the city!

Some people with an interest in lepidoptera have developed a hobby of rearing butterflies to the chrysalis stage and then taking them to shut-ins and hospitalized patients. The experience of seeing a chrysalis transformed into a living butterfly can be an inspiration to people waiting to be made well, helping them to turn their thoughts outward, away from their own troubles, and restoring some hope for recovery.

A child's first contact with the natural

world is likely to be through flowers—witness the countless dandelions and violets brought home, clutched in small, sweaty fists—and from flowers may easily come the child's first caterpillar or the first butterfly seen nectaring. Nature walks with the whole family on a Sunday afternoon can easily lead to taking home a caterpillar, and so begins a new adventure in a new world. The adult who becomes familiar with the local butterflies and helps children find and enjoy them will become the Pied Piper of the neighborhood. Sharing and fostering children's natural interest in caterpillars, in their funny faces, the way they feel, the tickly way that they walk (fig. 2–2), and helping them witness the transformations yet to come, can shape the child's outlook on insects—and perhaps on the whole natural world—as forms of life to be respected and enjoyed, rather than as vermin to be crushed beneath the heel.

Many naturalists now feel that numbers and diversity among lepidoptera and the balance among species are the most sensitive indicators of the overall health of an environment. Spring becomes silent as a result of man's injudicious contamination, pollution, and destruction of the biosphere, and, in addition, it has become apparent that the spring azure (*Celastrina ladon*) no longer flits along the woodland path, the orange-tip (*Falcapica midea*) no longer hurries across the grassy glade, and the pale green luna moth (*Actias luna*) no longer beats against the window screen at night. A decrease in the variety and numbers of butterflies and moths in an environment is a strong indication of its decline. The observations of amateur "lep-watchers," repeated systematically over a number of years, can play a significant part in monitoring such changes.

Figure 2–2 "The tickly way that they walk"

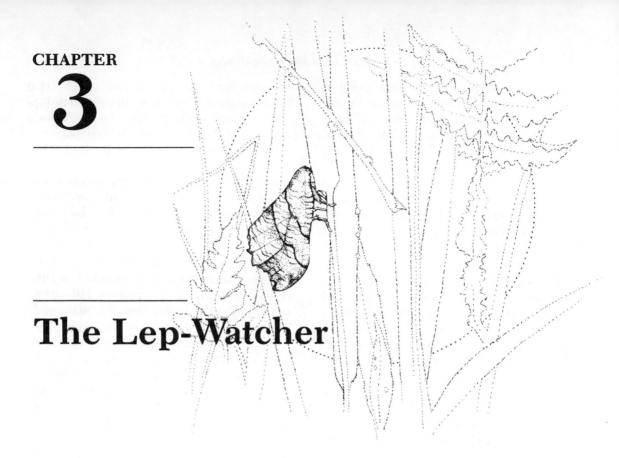

The Lep-Watcher

Figure 3–1 Two-lined hooktip (*Drepana bilineata*)

The practice of bird-watching is a familiar one. Bird-watchers set up feeders where they can see them easily from their windows, and they stock them with food to attract birds. They put out birdhouses so that they can watch them raise their young. They plant trees and bushes to provide shelter and food. They go out into the countryside, equipped with binoculars, notebooks, cameras, and even tape recorders, in order to observe the birds in situations as undisturbed as possible. They visit special habitats in search of particular species. Some bird-watchers plan vacations around opportunities to observe birds in other parts of the country; some have even been known to scuttle important business engagements in order to view an unusual species in some far-off place.

Butterfly- and moth-watchers, or lep-watchers, do most of these things, often with the same manifestations of addiction seen in bird-watchers. They use binoculars less often, since most observing can be done at very short range, and the tape recorders can be left behind—a very few species of lepidoptera make significant sounds. In their gardens, lep-watchers plant flowers, shrubs, and trees that will be attractive to moths and butterflies, either as sources of nectar on which the adults can feed, or as food plants for the caterpillars. They may leave a woodpile undisturbed through the winter as a hibernation place for anglewing butterflies. They put out food (bait) to attract butterflies and moths. They roam as far and as near as the bird-watchers, and for the same reasons.

One of the prime attractions of bird-watching is the camaraderie of going afield with others with similar interests, of learning from others who have had different opportunities to observe, and of making new friends in unfamiliar places. For bird-watchers this is quite easy, through the Audubon Society and through local bird-club listings. Because there are fewer lepidopterists and lep-watchers, finding other interested people, even in one's own neighborhood, can seem difficult. However, with the help of the Lepidopterists' Society (see page 175) and its affiliated local groups, a network of such people, throughout the country and the world, can readily be discovered.

There is no line drawn between bird-watchers and lep-watchers. More and more bird-watchers are beginning to pay attention to the butterflies that cross their paths, and many butterfly-watchers keep one eye on the birds. In colder climates, many lep-watchers turn to bird-watching in the winter, when low temperatures force the butterflies and moths into hibernation.

There is another reason why lep-watchers keep one eye on the birds. Most birds are lep-watchers, too. They depend upon lepidoptera in all stages for their livelihood. Nuthatches, chickadees, and creepers search tree bark for eggs and larvae. Warblers and orioles harvest caterpillars from leaves. We have seen one oriole take as many as thirty small inch worms per minute from an infested oak. Cuckoos enjoy some of the fuzzy caterpillars spurned by other birds.

Woodpeckers search out hidden pupae. Many species, not just flycatchers, go after moths and butterflies on the wing and at rest. They are not always successful, as evidenced by the beak marks identifiable on the wings of many specimens, yet all lep-watchers, sooner or later, are thwarted by some bird that snatches a larva or butterfly they are watching intently or trying to photograph.

We have a friend who is a bird-watcher, and also a plant-watcher at the Arnold Arboretum in Boston. He rears plants. We rear butterflies. We managed to awaken his interest in butterflies by introducing him to one of our most intriguing inhabitants, a caterpillar of the spicebush swallowtail (*Papilio troilus*). When full grown, this caterpillar is endowed with "eyespots," cryptic coloring (camouflage), and forked scent glands (osmeteria) that it can extrude when threatened. These characteristics cause it to resemble a small snake, and thus it is supposedly protected from bird predators. A day or so after our friend had been charmed by one of these handsome larvae, he came face to face with another caterpillar of the same species in his own yard. Fired with hope and enthusiasm, he rushed for his camera, brought the little creature into critical focus at close range in broad sunlight, and flexed his finger to click the shutter. At that same instant, a bluejay swooped down from a tree, grabbed the caterpillar in its beak, and disappeared! Needless to say, this was a traumatic experience for a novice lepidopterist—the picture came out a complete blur.

A major difference between bird-watching and lep-watching is in identification of species. One doesn't think of capturing a bird in order to identify it. That practice is illegal and may result in significant harm to the bird or its young. It is also unnecessary because of the excellent field guides available. Excellent guides are available for lepidoptera also (see the bibliography starting on page 183), but the differences between species are often so subtle and the time for observation so brief that accurate sight identification is far less reliable than with birds. Fortunately, using proper techniques (see part V, "Tricks and Tools"), it is possible to capture a moth or butterfly, examine it in considerable detail, and release it unharmed. This can be done without any effect on the individual or its offspring. The lepidopteran will soon resume its mating or egg-laying activities, and eggs, once deposited, need no further attention from the parent. With this advantage, some people, even though they choose to be strictly watchers, or to collect only on film, may at times decide to collect specimens so that they may be more certain of what they are watching.

CHAPTER 4

Botany, Geology, and Lepidoptera

Figure 4–1 New England buck moth (*Hemileuca lucina*) laying eggs

The ties between plants and lepidoptera are very close. Some flowers depend largely or entirely on moths or butterflies for pollination. For the most part, the pollen is carried casually from flower to flower, adhering to the tongue, to hairs about the head, and to the legs. Occasionally it is transferred in a very deliberate manner, as is the case with the yucca moth (*Tegeticula yuccasella*), described in chapter 7. The primrose moth (*Schinia florida*) rests by day within the blossoms of the common evening primrose, transferring pollen as it moves from flower to flower. While this plant is in large part self-pollinated, the moth is probably responsible for any cross-pollination that does occur. Its larvae eat the primrose seed heads.

In Madagascar, there is an orchid with such a narrow, deep throat that when it was discovered it appeared that only an insect with a tongue at least 10″ long could pollinate it. Eventually a very large sphinx moth was discovered with a tongue that long. It was given the name *Macrosilia morgagni predicta*.

One plant changes the color of its flowers in order to attract a moth. The scarlet gilia of the Southwest attracts hummingbirds to its bright red flowers. After midsummer, when the hummingbirds have moved away, the plants are able to produce pale pink flowers, which are more attractive to the white-lined sphinx moth (*Hyles lineata*), its principal late-season pollinator.

While lepidoptera are important to many plants, plants are absolutely essential to the existence of most butterflies and moths, which depend upon them for food, both as larvae and as adults. Virtually all parts of plants are used as food by one group or another.

12

The eggs of a very large majority of lepidoptera are laid on leaves. If they are laid on plants valued by people, this can be an aggravation, and sometimes a disaster. The havoc in the tomato patch is the work of the tomato hornworm (*Manduca quinquemaculata*). The lacework in the broccoli leaves hails the coming of the cabbage butterfly (*Pieris rapae*) or the cabbage looper moth (*Trichoplusia ni*). Caterpillars of the orange sulphur butterfly (*Colias eurytheme*) have been known to attack the alfalfa crops in the Imperial Valley of California in massive swarms. During one research project there, the workers found the chrysalids so numerous that they gathered them from the plants and stacked them in pyramids three feet high.

Forest pests such as the gypsy moth (*Lymantria dispar*) and the spruce budworm (*Choristoneura fumiferana*) can be even more damaging, for they can defoliate vast areas when unchecked. This was the case in 1983 in the Allegheny Mountains, when gypsy moths completely stripped the woodlands for a distance of ninety miles along the Pennsylvania Turnpike, giving the July woods the appearance of December. The spruce budworm is nearly as great a menace to northern forest lands. In some years the damage done to growing branch tips is so great as to kill the majority of the spruce and fir trees.

In the state of Washington, outbreaks of the pine white butterfly (*Neophasia menapi*) periodically cause widespread forest damage. An outbreak during the following year can usually be predicted by a sudden increase in the number of caterpillars found pupating on the ground.

The most spectacular of our native moths, the silk moths (Saturniidae), the sphinx moths (Sphingidae), and the underwings (genus *Catocala*) are all leaf eaters, but rarely inflict enough damage to qualify as significant pests. They can, however, be called nuisances. The handsome buck moths (genus *Hemileuca*) are not all bothersome, but one species, called the range caterpillar (*H. oliviae*), in periodic outbreaks consumes all the grasses on the cattle ranges of large areas of northeastern New Mexico.

Flower buds are the diet of the caterpillars of the spring azure butterfly (*Celastrina ladon*), which needs a succession of food plants—at least three, one for each of three successive broods. The first of the food plants are flowering dogwood, wild cherry, or one of the early viburnums. The second brood selects the early summer dogwoods, viburnums, and sumach, while the midsummer brood uses meadowsweet. In each case, the eggs are carefully laid between the buds of the flower clusters. The female butterfly first tests the plant by stamping on it and will not oviposit until she finds the buds at a particular stage of growth. When the eggs hatch, the caterpillars need to crawl into the buds before they open, to feed on the hidden petals. They then drop to the ground and pupate in leaf debris.

Larvae of many of the flower moths (genus *Schinia*) feed within the receptacles of fully open flowers, pushing up the center florets into a disorderly heap.

Although the great majority of lepidopteran larvae feed on leaves, the ravages do not stop there. Some larvae bore into the stems or roots of soft plants; some are even aquatic feeders, boring into the stems of water lilies! Carpenterworms (cossids) spend two to four years boring in living hardwood trees and are able to make tunnels the diameter of a finger. Ferns are not commonly used for larval food by moths, but a few species of noctuid and geometrid larvae eat the foliage, and certain species of borer moths (genus *Papaipema*) feed within the roots. Lichen moths (some of the arctiids) eat lichens, and fungus moth larvae (genus *Metalectra*) eat woody fungi. Even dead vegetable matter is not wasted, for the larvae of many deltoid moths feed upon leaf litter on the forest floor.

With few exceptions, adult moths and butterflies take nourishment only through the long, tubular proboscis that supplants the chewing mandibles of the caterpillar. Nectar, sap from trees, and juices from rotting fruit are all components of the daily diet of adult lepidoptera. Variety in the menus of moths and butterflies appears to be endless.

Answers to the questions "What kind of moth or butterfly?" and particularly "What kind of caterpillar?" hinge upon the plants with which the species is associated. Lep-watchers find themselves becoming unavoidably interested in the plants around them; they are soon using field guides not just for moths and butterflies, but for flowering plants and for trees and shrubs as well. Lepidopterists often become ardent botanists in their zeal to learn more about life cycles. Plants that have been overlooked or ignored because they are not particularly showy or fragrant suddenly become important, and in turn add to the lepidopterist's enjoyment.

Geological features—details of the lie of the land—play a major part in the dis-

tribution of moths and butterflies. The south-facing, north side of a river valley may have species not present on the cooler, south side or on the uplands. Hilltops attract butterflies seeking mates. Gullies and canyon bottoms may be thronged with butterflies in need of water.

Geological features have an important effect on plant growth. Plant species and plant communities are dependent on the soil on which they grow. The character of the soil is, in turn, determined by underlying geological features. A soil may be acid or alkaline, well drained or waterlogged, or have any of dozens of other characteristics depending on what lies beneath it.

The lepidopterist who understands the need of the northern metalmark (*Calephelis borealis*) for a ragwort that grows on limestone ledges will not go looking for that butterfly in an acid bog. On the other hand, the acid bog, if it supports a growth of cranberry, would be the right place to look for the bog copper (*Lycaena epixanthe*). As you look for species utilizing specialized habitats, an interest in geology develops automatically.

Lepidoptera depend upon plants, plants depend upon soil, and the soil is influenced by the underlying rock and hydrological features. Because of this inescapable interdependence, the lepidopterist painlessly becomes a botanist, and the botanist a geologist!

PART **II**

Habits, Habitats, and Hazards

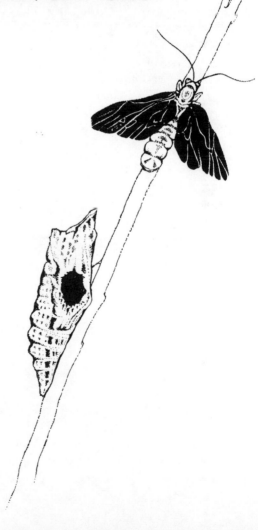

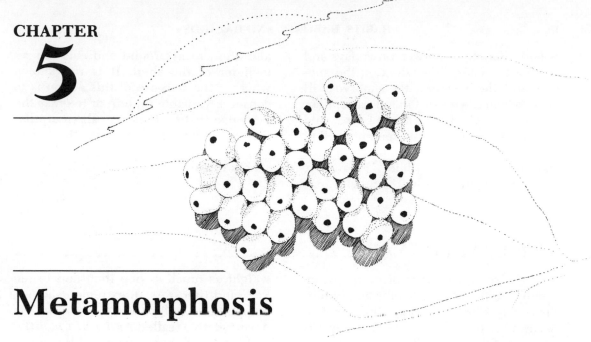

Metamorphosis

Figure 5–1 Io moth eggs (*Automeris io*)

In an often-quoted cartoon, two caterpillars are conversing as they watch a butterfly glide overhead. One says to the other, "You'll never get me up in one of those things!"

Obviously that caterpillar had no understanding of its own metamorphosis, which (judging by its caricature in the cartoon) was nearly finished.

THE EGG

The eggs of lepidoptera vary greatly in size, shape, and decoration, but all serve the same purpose: to provided a sheltered environment within which the embryo can develop into a tiny caterpillar, equipped to fend for itself. The main elements of the egg are an outer shell to give physical protection, a waxy layer to limit water loss, a system of ventilating pores to allow the embryo to obtain air, and a yolk supply to provide food for the development of the embryo.

The shell is formed in the ovary of the

female before the egg has been fertilized and contains an almost invisible perforation called the micropyle, through which spermatozoa enter the egg. This micropyle can sometimes be recognized with the help of a hand lens.

A few of our small hairstreak butterflies and a large number of moths hibernate as eggs, but the majority of the eggs of lepidoptera hatch during the spring and summer months, and sometimes into the fall. In most cases, the development of the embryo begins as soon as the egg is laid. Sometime between five days and two weeks later, depending on the species and the weather, the embryo will have become a fully formed caterpillar, ready to hatch. Using a hand lens, one can see it through its transparent shell at this time, as it moves about in the remaining embryonic fluid. Finally it chews a hole in the shell, struggles out, and often turns around and eats the remainder of the shell. It is not known whether the purpose of this action is to conserve valuable protein or to erase the evidence that there is a small caterpillar in the vicinity. In any case, the act of hatching is assurance that metamorphosis has begun.

THE CATERPILLAR

The Greek word *metamorphosis*, when applied to the lives of moths and butterflies, refers to the many changes that occur after the tiny caterpillar chews its way out of the eggshell.

These changes include five larval instars. An instar is the interval between the caterpillar's moults, or sheddings of its skin. On hatching from the egg, it is in its first instar. After feeding for a few days, it will shed its skin and will then be in its second instar. This process is repeated until the caterpillar reaches its fifth instar, having moulted four times.

The freshly hatched caterpillar, small though it is, seems too big to have been crammed into that tiny egg just a few minutes before. This incongruity is heightened in the case of hairy larvae. Their moist, limp fur coats dry and stiffen and suddenly spring upright, often without warning. Even more striking are the species decorated with filaments or horns, which are rapidly distended and thrust upward, like miniature periscopes, by hydraulic pressure. Hatching is, indeed, a point of no return!

Once out of the egg, the caterpillar settles into its primary role in life. It is an eating machine. In its few weeks of life as an eating, growing caterpillar, it will consume enough greenery to increase its weight as much as one thousand to ten thousand times. As an extreme example, our familiar polyphemus moth has an Asian relative (called *Antheraea mylitta*) that hatches from an egg weighing only a few milligrams. When fully grown it can weigh as much as 65,000 milligrams, or more than three ounces.

Each new moult is preceded by a day or so of languid rest, during which time the caterpillar neither eats nor moves about while a new and larger skin is growing beneath the old skin.

With the onset of each instar, the appearance of the caterpillar changes. Sometimes these changes are radical, sometimes not, depending on the kind of protection the particular species will need to stay alive throughout larval life.

When a caterpillar sheds its skin, it appears to be larger than it was before. It may look larger because the new skin, which had been forming under the discarded one, is wrinkled, giving the impression of bulk. Actually the caterpillar weighs less than before. During the last day before moulting, it had been resting while many changes were taking place inside its old skin, and during that time it had not eaten anything. Contrary to the conventional statement that "caterpillars grow by moulting," caterpillars grow by eating, thus filling the new skin that had been growing inside the old one before the moult.

As an example, the tobacco hornworm (*Manduca sexta*) is about four centimeters long at the beginning of its fifth instar. During the next five days, it almost doubles its length. At the same time, it increases its weight from one gram to ten grams. The skin of a caterpillar cannot stretch like a balloon. The caterpillar is able to grow larger partly by smoothing out the many tiny wrinkles present in the new skin, but even more by the actual growth of the skin itself, a fact only recently confirmed. This is very comforting. It was always difficult to look at a rapidly growing caterpillar and to accept the belief that its skin was not growing also!

The head of the caterpillar is a rigid, chitinous capsule that protects various organs of the butterfly, so far unformed, including the antennae, the proboscis, and the many-faceted global eyes of the butterfly-to-be. It is also equipped with several useful devices that will disappear before the butterfly emerges. For instance, there can be as many as six minuscule lenses (called ocelli) on each side of the head capsule, through which light enters, making it possible for the caterpillar to see light and orient itself in relation to the sun. There are also its mouth parts, called chewing mandibles, jaws that instead of biting up and down, chew from each side toward the middle, an ideal design for a tiny caterpillar that can only nip off bits from the leaf surface, but equally useful as it grows for chopping chunks from the full thickness of leaves. Some caterpillars (notably the Cossidae, a family of moths known as carpenterworm moths) can actually carve tunnels in living hardwood with those marvelously conceived mandibles.

Directly beneath the mandibles is the spinneret, an invaluable asset to the little creature that can barely distinguish light from dark. Wherever it goes, it moves its head from side to side incessantly, spinning a silken pathway to be used in retracing its steps and assuring a better foothold. Later the spinneret may be used for sewing leaves together to form a hideout; still later, when it prepares to pupate, a butterfly caterpillar will use it to form an anchor, and a moth caterpillar to spin its cocoon. After the last larval instar, the spinneret will vanish, for its usefulness will be over as soon as the chrysalis or cocoon has been formed.

The body of the caterpillar is divided into thirteen segments (fig. 5–2). Each of the first three segments (which constitute the thorax) is equipped with a pair of pointed, stubby legs that assist the caterpillar in walking. In the process of metamorphosis they will evolve into the long, slender legs of the moth or butterfly.

The remaining ten segments make up the abdomen. Of these, the first two bear no appendages. Segments 3–6 each have a pair of soft, stubby prolegs, which are the main walking legs of most caterpillars. The end of each proleg bears a ring of little hooks. These, combined with the silk it spins, make it possible for the caterpillar to walk at any angle, on almost any surface, without falling. Trying to detach one of these prolegs from a rough surface is difficult and apt to cause injury that could be fatal. At the tail end of the caterpillar, on the tenth abdominal segment, there is a pair of anal prolegs, claspers used by both moth and butterfly larvae as anchors when their larval skins are shed.

All of these structures will disappear at the time of formation of the pupae of

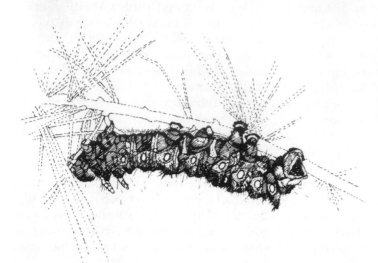

Figure 5–2 Imperial moth larva (*Eacles imperialis*), showing body segments and appendages (*left to right*): head; three thoracic segments bearing true legs; ten abdominal segments (1–8 marked with white spiracular spots), prolegs on segments 3–6; tenth abdominal segment bearing anal claspers

moths and the chrysalids of butterflies, and entirely new kinds of locomotive devices will replace them.

The caterpillar's manner of locomotion is intriguing. It walks from back to front, with a rippling motion, one pair of prolegs at a time. The anal pair lets go, moves forward, and grasps the twig again just as pair 4 lets go. Pair 4 displaces pair 3, and so on until the back half of the caterpillar has moved forward one step. As it then lets go with its three pairs of front legs, its front end is thrust forward with the help of the ripple behind it, and it takes a fresh foothold. The process is then repeated from behind. A caterpillar in a hurry sometimes seems to have two ripples going at once. Looper caterpillars or inchworms (geometrids) are so named because they move in a different fashion. They lack the first three pairs of prolegs and move the remaining fourth pair and the anal pair as a single unit. As the back end lets go, it moves forward to grasp the twig right behind the thoracic legs, bending the thin body up into an inverted loop like the Greek letter omega. The caterpillar then lets go with its front feet, pushes forward for a fresh hold, and humps along on its way, "measuring" as it goes.

THE PREPUPAL STADIUM

This is a period of unseen metamorphosis. Its onset can be predicted when the caterpillar stops feeding and remains quiescent. It begins to change color and has a slightly shriveled appearance, as if it were ill. Suddenly it excretes a large mass of semiliquid material consisting of the lining and the remaining contents of the gut, and remnants of the caterpillar's organs that will no longer be needed. It begins to wander, at first in slow and seemingly painful jerks, but after a time these change to an undulating gait.

Meanwhile, the transformation from caterpillar to pupa is beginning to take place. Phagocytes, small cells within the

Figure 5–3 Prepupal larva of gulf fritillary (*Agraulis vanillae*)

caterpillar's blood, begin to break down degenerating organs of the caterpillar and convert them into valuable amino acids and other molecules that are then used to form new cells for structures of the butterfly or moth.

All moths must hide during the pupal stage. Some bury themselves underground, shed their last larval skins in darkness, and transform into little brown pupae, some slender and pointed at the caudal (tail) end, some oval and more blunt. The regal and imperial moth larvae (*Citheronia regalis* and *Eacles imperialis*), like those of the sphinx moths, bury themselves underground and form pupae much larger than the chrysalids of the largest North American butterflies; all of these underground pupae are brown, like the earth that surrounds them.

The cocoons of the luna moth (*Actias luna*), the tulip-tree silk moth (*Callosamia angulifera*), and the cynthia moth (*Samia cynthia*) are each spun wrapped in a leaf of one of their various food trees. The caterpillars, working from within, spin little shelters that grow thicker until the innermost wall is solid, smooth, and egg-shaped. These cocoons later fall to the ground when the tree drops its leaves. The polyphemus moth (*Antheraea polyphemus*) is even more industrious. The cocoon walls it builds grow stiffer as the caterpillar exudes a substance that strengthens them still further as it dries. This cocoon usually falls to the ground also, but in some southern localities it remains hanging from a twig of its food tree.

The cocoon of the cecropia moth is still more heavily girded against unseen enemies and remains tightly attached to the chosen branchlet. Within these silk-lined "eggshells," these caterpillars shed their last larval skins. The pupae that result have the texture of rare and highly polished mahogany.

The caterpillars of butterflies also spin but do not form cocoons. They begin the change from caterpillar to chrysalis by spinning a tiny button of silk on a surface that will protect them by its location, a suface providing safety from the elements, space to hang, and camouflage against predators. They will then walk carefully over the button they have spun and hook their last pair of prolegs into it (fig. 5–3).

The caterpillar of a swallowtail (a papilionid) or of a sulphur butterfly (a pierid) will spin an extra support, a sort of seatbelt designed to hold its body close to the surface it has chosen. To make this belt it spins back and forth, each time holding the strand of silk between the first pairs of its pointed true legs, and each time attaching another strand of silk to its chosen surface, until the girdle becomes strong enough to support its body. Finally it ducks its head under the loop it has made and squirms about until the belt is properly adjusted across its back. Then, gradually releasing all but its anal prolegs, one pair at a time, it suspends itself in a commalike position, supported only by the belt and the silken button.

The last act of the caterpillar's existence is about to begin, the shedding of the last larval skin. As this is accomplished all traces of the caterpillar will disappear, and an entirely new form will take its place.

THE CHRYSALIS

For the last time, the caterpillar loosens its skin, pushing out the thorax as it splits, struggling to free the new self from the old. Little by little the old skin is cast, until it becomes a crumpled ball at the end of the body, still clinging to the silken button so recently spun. Holding the old skin tightly between two segments near the end of its new body, the little creature draws out a new device, a cremaster. This is a chitinous spike at the end of the abdomen, tipped with minute hooks that it thrusts into the silk button, twisting it about until it is secure. Then the old skin is released and falls to the ground. A newly built "cage" appears, inside which the butterfly can gradually grow and take form. This is the chrysalis.

If the chrysalis holds a monarch or one of the nymphalids, there will be no seat belt to steady and protect it through this greatest of hazards. The act of suspending its body from a tight pinhead of silk must be accomplished with perfect coordination and timing in a matter of seconds, while it hangs head down and sightless, reaching in midair for a fragment of silk spun by a creature now vanished (fig. 5–4).

And so the new chrysalis hangs, swinging slightly with every breeze, as though it forms a part of the leaf or twig to which it is attached. The nymphalids are shaped a little like miniature foxes, swaddled in clothes of the most exquisite shades and designs, often decorated with metallic silver or gold. The caterpillars of the painted lady (*Vanessa cardui*), a butterfly found throughout the world, sometimes change to chrysalids the color of pure gold. (The word "chrysalis" derives from *chrysos*, the word for gold in Greek and older languages.) In Mexico there is a black-and-white butterfly

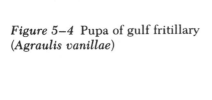
Figure 5–4 Pupa of gulf fritillary
(*Agraulis vanillae*)

(*Morpheis ehrenbergii*) related to our Baltimore checkerspot. Its chrysalis is a mosaic of gleaming black and white, a miniature Pierrot that dances when touched.

When the pupa of a moth finally bursts through the last larval skin, it is soft and rather shapeless, but within a few hours the outer surface hardens and assumes its characteristic color, rich brown in most moths, multicolored among the butterflies. As this hardening process proceeds, a multitude of other changes is taking place. Wing buds that were hidden within the caterpillar have turned inside out and are enlarging close to the surface of the pupa. Compound eyes are developing where only simple ocelli existed before. The chewing mandibles of the larva are replaced by the tubular tongue of the adult. The reproductive organs begin to mature. The shell of the chrysalis begins to harden, and a pattern of folded wings becomes clearly visible. The antennae, the two halves of the proboscis, and the legs of the imago lie together like thin pencil lines, between the edges of the wings—all but the proboscis of some sphinx moths, which are encased in a separate sheath and stand apart from the body like a jug handle. For the first time, there is tangible evidence that a moth or butterfly is on the way.

During this time of hardening, the little creature is very vulnerable to damage from external pressure from hard objects and rough surfaces. It is for this reason that the caterpillar spent many hours in the process of suspending itself in a safe

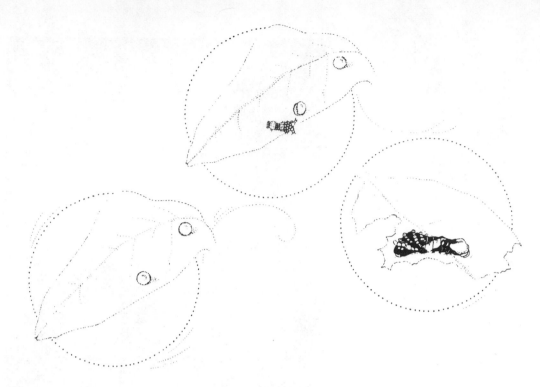

Figure 5–5 Metamorphosis cycle of giant swallowtail (*Papilio cresphontes*) (*clockwise from upper left*): eggs; newly hatched larva; middle instar larva; mature larva; prepupal stadium; pupa, with silk girdle; pupa bursting open; newly emerged butterfly; drying; fully expanded wings; preparing to fly

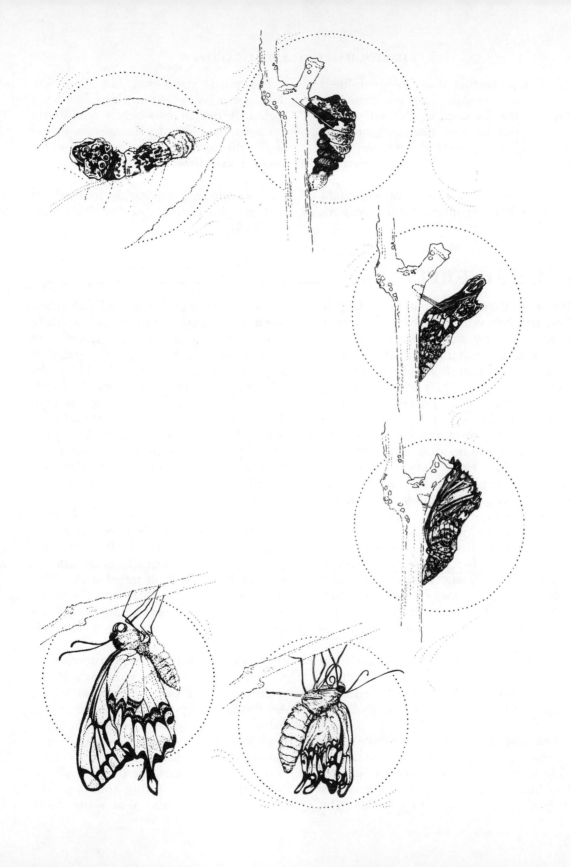

place or protecting itself in a silk-lined cocoon or smooth earthen chamber. Without this protection, the soft young pupa would become damaged, and the insect, when it emerged later, would be in some way deformed, perhaps even unable to fly. (See figure 15–1: the right forewing of the butterfly on the right shows a hole resulting from pupal injury.)

The pupal stage may last for a few days, a few weeks, or until the following spring. A day or two before a butterfly emerges, the chrysalis changes color, and finally the pattern and color of the wings become visible in miniature. This is the time to forget everything else and watch the seemingly impossible marvel of metamorphosis as it reaches its climax (fig. 5–5).

THE BUTTERFLY

Wherever they come from, be it deep in the earth, the underside of a leaf, a dark corner of some garage, against a sheltered wall, or from the shell-like lining of a cocoon, all emerging lepidoptera must find places where their wings can hang down. Every change during the process of metamorphosis is set by some inner clock, and failure in any step of the process is bound to result in deformity, and usually death. Each butterfly crawls to the nearest support, its diminutive wings dangling limply, its pendulous abdomen dragging behind; free of impediments at last, it hangs and waits.

The nymphalids and danaids hang head down in their chrysalis shells, and when these delicate, nearly transparent little cages begin to split apart, the butterflies have nothing to grasp except the shattered remains of the chrysalis. The butterfly moves, a long seam buckles and splits, an eye appears, and suddenly the little creature dives down headfirst, reaching wildly for a foothold, clinging desperately to the transparent shelter of its former life.

The first action a butterfly takes as it emerges is that of pumping blood into its wing veins, causing the wings to unfold. The little fingernail-size wings immediately begin to expand to full size. The

two sides of the proboscis coil and uncoil in rapid succession, uniting into a single tube as this new creature struggles to bring itself into being. In the space of just a few minutes, the strangely beautiful ordeal is over. The butterfly hangs still soft and helpless, its only defense the ability to open and close its still-limp wings. The blood is drawn back into the body, leaving the hollow veins to dry and harden. The crawling and the darkness are left behind, and the butterfly belongs to the air.

Moths whose pupae are loosely held by a few strands of silk between two or three leaves or within a cleft on the bark of a tree have an equally easy task. As soon as they split their pupal shells, they are free. This is the case with the gypsy moth pupa. If the caterpillar has spun a more elaborate cocoon, the situation is different. In some species, such as the cecropia, the cocoon is constructed with a crumpled, funnellike valve at the top, with the small end pointing outward. Anything trying to enter through the valve meets a hopeless tangle of silk, but the emerging moth can shoulder its way out with little difficulty.

In some instances, the pupal shell has rings of forward-pointing spines on the abdominal segments. When the moth emerges, these spines protect it from dragging the pupal shell out with it. A moth that is free, but with an unanchored pupal shell still adhering to its abdomen, may not be able to finish extricating itself. Such an individual will be unable to mate, and probably will not survive "the slings and arrows of outrageous fortune."

Other cocoons, such as those of the polyphemus moth or the commercial silkworm, are oval with densely woven eggshell-like inner walls and no escape valve. As these moths emerge, glands near the front of the head secrete an enzyme that softens and weakens the strands of silk so that the moth can burst through.

If pupation takes place in an earthen cell within the soil, the emerging moth is faced with the problem of reaching the surface so that it can spread its wings without damage. Emerging sphinx moths dig their way out, somehow doing so without damaging their soft, unexpanded wings, but the secrecy of this operation has been safely guarded from humans up to the present day. These are but a few of the many small miracles that make the study of lepidoptera such an intriguing pursuit and such a never-ending mystery.

CHAPTER

6

Broods

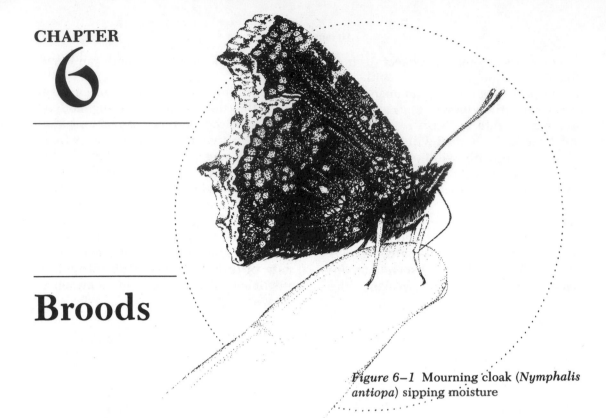

Figure 6–1 Mourning cloak (*Nymphalis antiopa*) sipping moisture

As a beginning butterfly watcher you will probably wander out into a sunny garden, meadow, or rural roadside just to see what may be there. Whether it is the right time for this species or that species is of little concern. It is the action that counts, and any butterfly you can observe is a prize. As you become familiar with particular species, you notice that one species, such as the orange-tip (*Falcapica midea*) may be around only in the spring, and that another species, such as the Baltimore (*Euphydryas phaeton*), doesn't appear until summer. Then you notice that a species, perhaps the mourning cloak (*Nymphalis antiopa*), that was present in the spring looking a little worn or tattered, disappears for a month or so, then reappears in summer, looking fresh and bright. The cabbage butterfly (*Pieris rapae*) seems to be around just about any time of the year when it is not

too cold. The idea of flight periods begins to emerge, and with it the subject of broods.

The term *broods*, in butterflies and moths, really refers to generations, not to the offspring of successive clutches of eggs as with domestic chickens. One complete cycle of metamorphosis is a generation, and the number of cycles that can occur in a year varies greatly in different species and in different localities. In the northern states, the luna moth emerges from its cocoon in May and June, and the fully grown larvae pupate in August. Their cocoons remain dormant until the following spring. Farther south where the growing season is longer, the moths emerge earlier, cocoons are formed by early summer, and there is time for a second brood to mature before frost, completing two cycles in a year. The luna is single-brooded in the north, but double-brooded in the south where edible hickory and walnut foliage is available for a longer season.

What about the orange-tip? It emerges in early spring, and the larvae have formed their thorn-shaped chrysalids by early June. There should be ample time for one or even two more broods before frost. This butterfly is single-brooded because the larval food plant, a diminutive cress, withers and dies with the onset of hot weather. If the butterfly emerged before the following spring, it would find no proper place to lay its eggs. Do not expect to find orange-tips in August!

This all looks very simple and straightforward until you come to the very common pearl crescent (*Phyciodes tharos*) and its much less common relative, the tawny crescent (*Phyciodes batesii*). The two butterflies look very much alike, and in some parts of New York state and Pennsylvania they occur in the same places and use the same species of asters as larval food plants. The pearl crescent emerges quite early in spring and breeds continuously until frost, having usually three broods per year at that latitude. The tawny crescent emerges in June and has but a single brood. Why? It remains for some butterfly watcher to discover the reasons.

In eastern Massachusetts, the red spotted purple (*Limenitis astyanax*) sometimes demonstrates another kind of cycling. Some larvae from one batch of eggs, feeding on wild black cherry, mature within a few weeks, pupate, and emerge ten days later as adults ready to mate and lay more eggs. Other larvae from the same batch feed more slowly, and in the second instar, while still very small, construct hibernacula in midsummer. A hibernaculum is a small, tubular shelter cut and sewn from the base of a leaf and secured to a twig by a silken

sheath. Within these shelters, the tiny caterpillars lie dormant for the rest of the summer, through the winter, and emerge in the spring to resume feeding voraciously. They then pupate. While this is going on, the eggs laid by their siblings the previous summer hatch, and the larvae feed into the second instar and make their own hibernacula by autumn. These then go through the winter and finish feeding in the spring side by side with their uncles and aunts. This kind of cycling is called a partial second brood. The early hibernators serve as a hedge against failure of the second brood due to inclement weather or a prematurely shortened season. The part of the brood that has gone "into storage" ensures perpetuation of the population the following year. A little farther south, where there is always time for two full broods, this precuation is unnecessary. Further north, where there is never time for a second brood to mature, the species is single-brooded.

Another variation, biennial brooding, occurs in some northern species such as the alpines (genus *Erebia*) and the arctics (genus *Oeneis*). In northern Minnesota, Macoun's arctic (*Oeneis macounii*) flies only in even-numbered years. Eggs laid in 1984, for example, hatch that summer. The larvae feed a while, hibernate, feed through the summer of 1985, hibernate again, and mature in the late spring, to emerge and fly as adults in the summer of 1986. In the summer of 1985 none of these butterflies are seen. The related polixenes arctic or Mt. Katahdin butterfly (*Oeneis polixenes*) in Maine has "overlapping" biennial broods. The butterflies are on the wing each summer, but larger numbers appear in the even-numbered years. If you plan a trip for butterfly watching in central or northern Alaska, consideration of this biennial brooding is important: about 35 percent of the species there fly only in the odd-numbered years.

Brood cycles are the rhythms in the lives of lepidoptera. Appreciating these rhythms sharpens the lep-watcher's skill in studying the species he seeks.

In the various brood cycles just described, there are often periods when the developing insect puts itself "on hold" and does nothing for an extended period. This period of inactivity is called *diapause*. It can occur in any stage of development, including the adult. Its timing varies with the species, with geography, with season, and even with local factors. It enables the insect to survive through a period when further development would be impossible or impractical. It can also serve as ensurance for survival of a population in the event of a local catastrophe.

If you walk along a woodland road on a warm, sunny day in late winter or early spring, you may see a large, mahogany-brown butterfly with pale borders on its angulated wings, a chain of bright blue dots bordering the brown. It drops to a sunny spot on the path and spreads its wings, basking in the warmth of the sun. It startles and flies off at your approach, but if you pause and wait, it returns to bask again in the same spot. With caution, you can approach more closely. Moisten a finger with saliva, move it slowly in front of its head, and the mourning cloak may climb upon your finger to drink.

Why is this butterfly here, with the pond still iced and winter not out of the ground? It has been in diapause, hibernating under the bark of a fallen tree and now roused out by the warming sun. It is already "old," as butterflies go, but its reproductive life is still ahead of it. It emerged from its chrysalis last August or September and has spent most of the time since then hidden quietly away, awaiting the advent of spring and fresh foliage on which its offspring can feed.

Have you ever found a mourning cloak flying about your living room in midwinter, or had one fly, slightly singed, from your fireplace? It had been hibernating in your woodpile, and you had brought its shelter indoors, unknowing.

In temperate climates, all species of moths and butterflies enter diapause during the cold season, but this winter diapause can also occur in any of the earlier developmental stages: pupa, larva, or egg, depending on the species. If you ski past the edge of a sassafras thicket or a stand of buttonbush, you may see a dangling, brown "dead leaf" the size of a date, silhouetted against the snow. When you inspect it more carefully, you see that it is a firm, dense, woven bag of silk, tied securely to its supporting twig, the cocoon of the promethea moth (*Callosamia promethea*, fig. 14–1). A similar structure dangling from the twig of an ailanthus by the railroad tracks in cities along the eastern seaboard is the cocoon of the cynthia moth (*Samia cynthia*). The tough, brown, spindle-shaped bag, the size of a mouse, attached tightly against a low twig of a beach plum or young wild black cherry may harbor a cecropia (*Hyalophora cecropia*). These cocoons protect the pupa within from the drying winter winds and offer some protection against mice and woodpeckers.

That brown-and-black woolly-bear caterpillar (*Pyrrharctia isabella*) you uncovered while raking up the leaves in November was also in its winter diapause, two-thirds grown and waiting to finish growing on the spring crop of dandelions and plantain. Yet some larvae do all their feeding either before or after the winter diapause. Those of single-brooded dusky wings (genus *Erynnis*) finish feeding in early summer, rest in a sewn-up nest of leaves that falls to the ground in autumn, and remain there among the leaf litter until pupation time in spring. At the other end of the scale, fritillary larvae (genus *Speyeria*) hatch from their eggs in fall, eat nothing, and remain on the ground until violet leaves unfold in April. So small as to be barely visible without a lens, they somehow avoid drying or drowning.

Some groups of noctuid moths, especially the pinions and some of the sallows (subfamily *Cuculliinae*), have two periods of diapause in their single-brooded annual cycle. Larvae, fully grown in June, spend the summer resting in the leaf litter or just under the surface of the soil in a summer diapause, "aestivation." Pupation occurs in late summer, and the moths emerge in autumn, fly for a few weeks, and then follow a hibernation pattern with winter diapause, similar to that of the mourning cloak.

The egg is the stage used for diapause by many species, witness the glossy brown, cuffed egg masses of the American tent caterpillar (*Malacosoma americanum*) on the twigs of your garden fruit trees, or the shaggy, pale-buff splotches left by the gypsy moths (*Lymantria dispar*) on your shade trees. Here the eggs lie dormant for nine or ten months until spring releases another generation for its annual feeding frenzy. The same pattern occurs in single-brooded hairstreak butterflies, but the eggs are laid singly in bark clefts or about the base of the food plant and come to our notice only by meticulous search or by watching the female deposit them.

Pupal diapause can present surprises. Some of a brood, instead of emerging on the expected schedule, will remain in diapause one or even two extra years. We have seen this happen with the buck moth (*Hemileuca maia*) in the East, with the sheep moth (*Hemileuca eglanterina*) in California, and with the eight-spotted forester (*Alypia octomaculata*), that handsome black-and-white pest from the walls of Ivy League colleges. A group of yucca moths was recently reported to have emerged after sixteen years in diapause!

This account of diapausal variations has been related for a purpose. When you are rearing moths and butterflies through their immature stages, ignorance or disregard of diapause requirements can lead to loss of an entire brood, or to wasting of individuals that would emerge later. Any pupae that seem at all alive (that have not dried to weightlessness or moldered away), even though motionless, should be dealt with patiently.

Knowing what to expect makes it easier to find and to rear lepidoptera successfully. Noting the unexpected and making records for future reference allow chance observations to become a part of the body of natural science.

CHAPTER
7

The Nonconformists

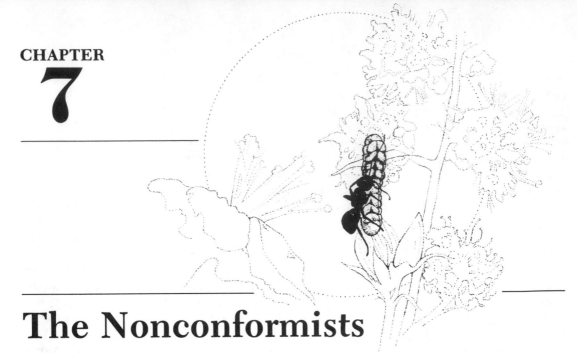

Figure 7–1 Ant tending spring azure larva (*Celastrina ladon*)

A yellow butterfly sails into the meadow and alights on a blossoming clover—then is off again to another one, trading pollen for nectar. For the flower that blooms, there is a butterfly to take its nectar and deliver its pollen.

A mass of small, squirming caterpillars feed together on a nearly leafed-out tree, leaving part of it unclad. Every caterpillar, large or small, that eats a leaf returns its remains to the ground, a contribution, however insignificant, however infinitesimal, to the enrichment of the earth.

Sometimes after sundown we go out in the woods and paint the trees with moth bait. An hour or so later, taking the same route, we see the *Catocala* moths, their red-and-black wings spread, their forewing camouflage melting into the bark of the tree—a ritual in hidden peace that perhaps no one has ever before seen performed by these particular moths.

Sometimes, along the highway, dozens or even hundreds of moths gather around the great mercury vapor lamps, as if maneuvering for position. We watch their frantic ballet, wondering why there is such an explosion of energy when daylight will see the ground below strewn with the dead? Why do they conceal themselves from the sunlight, which has so much more to offer? The great sphinx moths must feed at night, unseen. The silk moths, whose wings have a far more classic splendor than those of butterflies, are sometimes seen resting, spread against a wall if they have just emerged, but almost never are they seen flying during the day.

The smallest of moths are frequently seen rising out of the deep grass when one is walking through a meadow, but most moths live their lives in darkness. If they do take nectar, they do it at night, and their habits are kept secret.

UNUSUAL LIFE-STYLES

Secrecy in the realm of moths is wonderfully illustrated by the actions of the female yucca moth (*Tegeticula yuccasella*). It not only acts in secret, but provides one of the most unusual examples of the interdependence of plants and lepidoptera.

A little moth with pure white forewings, charcoal-gray hind wings fringed with pearl, and a wing span of only about an inch, it possesses all the organs found on the head of a moth—antennae, eyes, proboscis, palpi—and in addition is endowed with two unique, specialized organs that are pointed like miniature tusks. When ovopositing, the moth first pierces a hole in the pistil of a yucca blossom and lays an egg in the hole. Then with those stiff little tusks, or mandibular tentacles, as they are properly called, she gathers pollen and stuffs it into the hole. By doing so she not only covers and protects the egg but fertilizes the blossom. The egg hatches, and the flower produces seeds. The caterpillar feeds on some of the seeds, and those that remain fall to the ground to produce new plants.

This is a decidedly unusual variation of the egg-laying process, and the combination of using pistil, pollen, and seed to ensure the survival of a caterpillar is probably unique. It does illustrate the fact that no part of the plant is immune to attack, and that the art of egg laying is not always a matter of merely depositing an egg on a leaf.

The secrecy of most moths provides protection from diurnal predators, but the life-style of certain species often invites sudden death. Many a diligent housewife, on hearing the word "moth" immediately thinks, "Moths! My blankets! Did I remember to buy mothballs?"

It certainly seems that for a moth to spend its entire larval life eating woolen blankets or clothing of whatever color, texture, or age would be utterly unrewarding, but this is indeed how the all-too-familiar case-making clothes moth (*Tinea pellionella*) and the webbing clothes moth (*Tineola bisselliella*) live very comfortably. Their appetites are insatiable. If these species should invade your home while you are taking a vacation in Florida, your woolens, carpets, feathers, furs, silks, even shaving brushes, could be rendered useless. And yet these moths are so small that their average wingspan is less than two-thirds of an inch.

There is also the Indian-meal moth (*Plodia interpunctella*) that makes its dwelling in grain bins. It can even find its way into your kitchen and turn your box of oatmeal into a zoo, or suddenly fly out of your bag of flour.

The greater wax moth (*Galleria mellonella*) is not the type that enters your home, but its food preference, and its life-style and method of sustaining it are certainly unusual. The female flies about until she finds a neglected bee hive and lays her eggs on the honeycombs. When the caterpillars hatch, they wander over the combs, feeding on the wax as they go, at the same time using their spinnerets to lay a silken web over the combs.

Ever since the beginning of life on earth, living creatures have been developing life-styles calculated to ward off the extinction of their species. Everything alive today is a tribute to their success. The variety of ploys evolved by insects for the continuation of species is enormous, and such effort is in itself a small miracle. Of the countless habitats that have been occupied, one of the most compact is that of a tiny moth by the name of *Carpocapsa saltitans*, a native of Mexico. Its food plant is a member of the spurge family (genus *Sebastiana*). This little moth is probably the only insect responsible for the name of its food plant: the Mexican jumping bean.

The "beans" are actually sectors of a three-seeded fruit. When ripe, the fruit separates into three hard-shelled triangular sections. Each section is flat on two sides and rounded on the third.

When the beans first appear, the female moth lays her eggs on the soft outside shell. She may lay only one, or one on each section. When the tiny caterpillar hatches, it immediately bores a hole in the shell of the bean and eats its way inside. It consumes the kernel but leaves the shell intact. When it has finished eating, it spins a silken lining around the inside of the bean and hooks its anal prolegs into one side of it. The caterpillar then jerks its body forcibly from side to side. This violent activity, along with the shape of the bean, is what causes the bean to jump around, as far as six inches per jump.

These gymnastics continue until the caterpillar is ready to pupate. It sheds its skin, and the jumping stops. When the moth emerges, it crawls out into the sunlight through the same hole it made in the bean on the first day of its life as a caterpillar. It crawls out onto the ground, its wings still crumpled and no larger than a flake of ash, an insignificant breath of life—but what it did was not insignificant.

One European butterfly has such a strange habit that it cannot be overlooked. This is the lovely alpine butterfly *Parnassius apollo*. Its body is stout, clothed in soft, silky furlike hairs. Its antennae are unusually short, terminating in large, black clubs. Its forewings are creamy white and coal black with broad transparent borders. The forewings are decorated with large eyespots, some all red, others with white pupils and black rims. They are found only in the highest of mountains, and they nectar in the alpine meadows, flying from blossom to blossom, sometimes sinking to the ground to bask with spread wings.

The habit that makes them unique is that, during copulation, the male exudes a substance onto the end of the female's abdomen. It hardens to a waxlike consistency, and when copulation ends it remains secured to the abdomen, making it impossible for her to mate again. This structure, the *sphragis*, is produced by all male parnassians, including the North American ones. In each species it is a slightly different shape, but for the individuals in any one species it is always the same. Strangely enough, the male dies shortly after mating has finished— whether from exhaustion or ecstasy is not known. The female cannot remove the sphragis and must wear it for the rest of her life. This may amount to a week or so, until her egg laying is completed.

There are close to thirty species of blue lycaenids in North America. Of these, the most widespread and possibly the best known is the tiny spring azure (*Celastrina ladon*). This small butterfly thrives all over Canada and the United States, with the exception of southern Florida. It is one of the first butterflies to appear in the spring—a harbinger of spring, perhaps. It is always in the garden when the very first flowers are in bloom. It has varying numbers of broods per season, depending upon where it lives, but this hardy little butterfly seems to be present almost all summer. One thing is certain, in New England it is always around in midsummer when the meadowsweet is in bloom. Meadow-sweet has little clusters of pink blossoms each no broader than $\frac{1}{12}''$ across. The buds are no larger than a pinhead, but the little butterfly knows when they are just right for egg laying. She deposits only one egg on a cluster, tucking it between two buds, where it is invisible to the naked eye. When the little caterpillars hatch, they chew holes in the buds but damage only a very few. When they blossom, the caterpillar is hidden among them, invisible.

By the time the caterpillar reaches the fifth instar, it is sometimes bright green, handsomely decorated with a stripe of lighter green and dark red, or it is white with a similar stripe of pink. The caterpillar has a special gland near the end of its abdomen, which exudes a sweet liquid, much sought after by ants, which can detect it from a fair distance. The ants locate the caterpillar and imbibe its nectar. In return they groom the caterpillar, removing any parasites, mites, or other annoyances from its skin. This is one of the few instances in which two entirely different insects have each developed a maverick way of life that is beneficial to the other.

Several species of lycaenids are equipped with this "honey gland," but none of our species have as grotesque a relationship as one of the European blues.

Until recently there existed in England a butterfly called the large blue (*Maculinea arion*). For 150 years it had been a familiar sight in various parts of the country. Old records show that it was known to occur on ninety different sites, but by 1950 only thirty sites remained where the butterfly still flew. By 1960 the number had diminished to four sites, and in 1979 the butterfly was declared extinct in England.

The complexity of the life-style of this butterfly and the circumstance of its demise seem so bizarre as to be impossible, but the butterfly did exist in England and still exists in other parts of Europe. The remarkable circumstances necessary for the butterfly's survival were discovered by F. W. Frowhawk, a famous British naturalist.

The female butterfly lays her eggs in June on buds of wild thyme. The newly hatched caterpillars are almost perfectly camouflaged among the blossoms, which they begin to eat as soon as they hatch. When a little older, they will also eat their siblings, the largest eating the smaller ones.

During the third instar, a honey gland near the end of the caterpillar's abdomen begins to secrete "honeydew." This attracts various ants, which at first tend it in the manner of those tending the spring azure.

After moulting into the fourth instar, the caterpillar rests for several hours, leaves its food plant, and wanders in an aimless fashion. At this point it has grown to a length of slightly more than $\frac{1}{8}''$. Eventually it is discovered by a red ant, *Myrmica sabuleti*, the only species that can perform the following sequence of events successfully.

The ant strokes the honey gland of the caterpillar. It drinks the droplets. Soon the caterpillar puffs out its thorax, but not its abdomen. The ant straddles the caterpillar, picks it up, and carries it to the underground ant nest, where it will live in complete darkness the rest of its caterpillar life.

By now the caterpillar has lost the ability to be a vegetarian and begins to eat ant larvae. This goes on for six weeks, until the caterpillar becomes a fat, white grub; still it does not moult. It joins the remaining ant larvae and goes into hibernation until spring, still in the fourth instar.

It awakens, eats more and more ant larvae, and becomes pink, shiny, smooth, and even more bloated. It is now more than ½" long, and still in its fourth instar. Instead of moulting again, it climbs to the "ceiling" of the underground ant tunnel, spins a silk pad, and grips it with its tiny claspers. A week later, it finally sheds its skin and becomes a chrysalis. In June, it falls to the floor of the tunnel and remains immobile among the ants. It has been in total darkness since August. Then one day it bursts through the tightness of its chrysalis shell and somehow finds its way to the light, apparently with no help from the ants. When it finally reaches the surface, it climbs onto the nearest stem and stretches its wings.

> Out of the night that covers me,
> Black as the Pit from pole to pole,
> I thank whatever gods may be
> For my unconquerable soul.*

Extinction occurred in 1979 despite massive efforts to save the last colony. Too many adverse natural factors were involved.

The *sabuleti* ants and the caterpillars of the large blue need a habitat that is thoroughly grazed. In the late 1950s, disease reduced the rabbit populations that had normally assisted in this task. Grazing by sheep became uneconomical, and the grass grew too tall for these ants. Their numbers declined, and they were replaced by *M. scabrinodis*, another ant of the same genus. These crowded into the site, but they could not meet the needs of the caterpillars.

Even though the wild thyme was able to persist, these few changes of habit and habitat were enough to wipe out England's last remaining colony of the large blue butterfly.

As far as has been proven, only one North American butterfly has the carnivorous tendency of the large blue. This one is the harvester (*Feniseca tarquinius*). It has a wingspan of 1¼" at best, is orange and brown above, and is marked with delicate white rings beneath.

For its food it depends entirely on the white woolly aphids seen in large colonies on older twigs during the summer months. The caterpillar insinuates itself into one of these colonies. Some of the aphid "wool" brushes off onto its hairy coat, thus helping to conceal it from possible attack by ants. It then proceeds to eat the aphids until it is ready to pupate. (The pupa has a strange resemblance to the head of a monkey.) When the butterfly emerges, it feeds on honeydew produced by the aphids.

MALE/FEMALE VARIATIONS

In the adults of some species, there is variation in pattern or color between the sexes, a condition known as *sexual dimorphism*. The male promethea moth (*Callosamia promethea*) is brownish black, while the female is deep rose. The forewings of the male io moth (*Automeris io*) are yellow; those of the female are brown. The female carpenterworm moth (*Prionoxystus robiniae*) has wings shaped like a noctuid, the hind wings pale gray. The wings of the male are sphinx-like, with the hind wings yellowish orange.

Among the butterflies, the females of some blues are actually brown. Others

---

*From "Invictus," by W. E. Henley.

bear black or orange markings where the males are plain blue. The females of some species of coppers have forewings heavily spotted with brown, against a shimmering brassy or coppery ground; the forewings of the males may be only faintly spotted, upon a field of brown with a purplish sheen. The common cabbage butterfly (*Pieris rapae*) displays one black spot on the forewing of the male, but two on each female forewing.

Sulphurs carry the distinctions somewhat further. Males commonly have a neat, solid black band along the outer edges of the wings. In the females of many species this band may be broader and broken up with "holes" through which the yellow or orange ground color of the wing shows. In other species, the band is so pale and vague as to be barely visible. And in many species a considerable percentage of the females manifest still another variation. *Albinism* occurs: the yellow or orange ground color is replaced by white.

Perhaps the ultimate in dimorphism occurs in the fritillaries (genus *Speyeria*). There the tawny ground color of the female has a more yellowish cast than that of the male, and the brown spots and markings are heavier. Diana, however, goes her own way. The female *Speyeria diana* is steel blue and black, the male orange and brown. A more striking couple is not to be found among our lepidoptera.

UNUSUAL OUTCOMES

If, by some quirk of fate, you should find yourself in the right place at the right time, you might be able to net a specimen very rarely seen, which would make you the envy of your fellow collectors and be a rare showpiece in your own collection.

Occasionally a butterfly will deviate from the norm because of a malfunction of some sort in the process of metamorphosis. Sometimes these differences will be slight and easily overlooked. One such butterfly turned up while we were rearing some pipe vine swallowtails (*Battus philenor*). I noticed that on the underside of each hind wing there was a light-gray spot about the size of a dime, where it should have been black. This was a very small deviation, but we have never seen another one like it.

Another condition rarely seen in the field, but often seen in museum collections, is *melanism*, so called because the butterfly has much more black scaling on its wings than is normal. Melanism is caused by a variation in the development of the wing scales. It can be slight, as though the pattern were a bit blurred, while in extreme cases the butterfly can be transformed by it and cannot be truly identified until captured and studied.

The tiger swallowtail is an example. Its stunning yellow wings, streaked with black, make it one of the best known of our large butterflies. Its pattern is so clear-cut that any aberrant features can be detected at a glance. The tiger is indeed particularly susceptible to several forms of melanism. It may appear simply as a light dusting over its four wings, giving it a slightly "dirty" appearance. Sometimes the forewings are black and the hindwings are normal (yellow with a band of iridescent blue). Others have perfectly normal wing scaling on one side of the body, while the opposite wings are both totally black. There are also many instances in which areas of

Figure 7–2 Aberrant tiger swallowtail
(*Papilio glaucus*); normal form above

yellow and black are as disorderly as spilled paints (fig. 7–2).

Such alteration in normal color is seen only infrequently, but many species, ranging from the tiger to at least one of our small lycaenids, are susceptible to it. We were exploring a marsh in Vermont when a small cream-colored butterfly, obviously a lycaenid, appeared. It proved to be a "blonde" female of the bronze copper (*Hyllolycaena hyllus*), our largest copper butterfly. We brought it home, and it laid several eggs on knotweed, the larval food plant. The offspring all had normal copper-colored wings.

Any aberrant butterfly or moth should be kept and properly mounted and labeled with the date and place where it was caught. Insect geneticists are greatly interested in deviations from the norm, in whatever form.

A second and rarer genetic error—one which is found exceedingly infrequently —is the *bilateral gynandromorph* (Greek for "female-male-form"). In this case the butterfly or moth is half male and half female. The division occurs down the central axis of the insect's body, from head to tail, from the antennae, which differ between male and female in some species, to the genitalia at the end of the abdomen. One such butterfly was found in Canada, a yellow sulphur on one side, and the white female form on the other— a striking example! Even more dramatic was a gynandromorph Diana fritillary, with the blue-and-black female wings on one side, the orange-and-brown male wings on the other.

If, as in some moths, the female and male are not normally of the same size, one pair of wings will be larger than the other in cases of gynandromorphism. We have a gypsy moth gynandromorph in which the left antennae is female and the right one male, the left wings white and the right ones brown; the legs are female (black) on the left side and male (buff) on the right. This is a particularly interesting one, since the larger wings belong to the female, which seldom, if ever, uses them for flying. We wondered whether this insect, in flight, might have flown in circles!

One of the rarest and strangest of all malformations is the butterfly that, at the time of pupation, fails to shed the larval head capsule. When it emerges from its chrysalis and expands its wings, the capsule remains, enclosing the butterfly's head. Therefore the butterfly can neither see nor eat and has no antennae to pick up chemical signals. The future looks dark for a butterfly in this condition!

Seek and Ye Shall Find

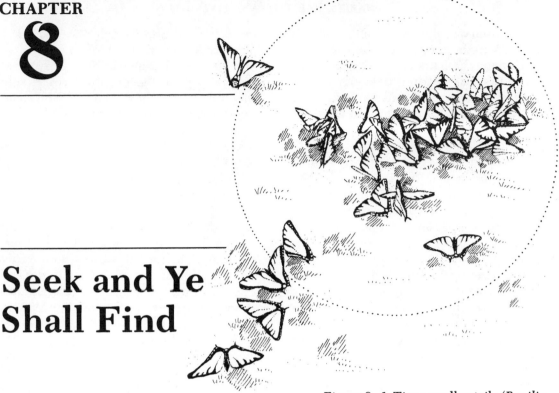

Figure 8–1 Tiger swallowtails (*Papilio glaucus*) "puddling"

Finding moths and butterflies can involve nothing more complex than taking a pleasant walk in the fields and woods and seeing what you chance upon. Some of your most interesting discoveries will be made in this way. But if you can become acquainted with the various activities on which the insect spends its time, you can be at the right places at the right times and leave much less to chance.

FEEDING

It is hard for most people to think of butterflies without thinking of flowers, and for lepidopterists the converse is equally true. Most butterflies do all or some of their feeding from the nectar of flowers, and it is while they are feeding that they are easiest to locate, to observe, and to photograph. Moths also depend a great deal on flower nectar for food, but this is less obvious, because so much of the feeding goes on after dark. Night-feeding moths cannot compete with sunlit butterflies as colorful spectacles. But the ghostly sight of a sphinx moth hovering at milkweed, viewed in the beam of a flashlight, or the coppery glint from the eyes of nectaring noctuids is no less intriguing.

As with bees, the feeding activities of moths and butterflies result in transfer of

39

pollen from one flower to another. It may be stuck to the tongue, the legs and feet, and among the hairs and scales about the head. Because feeding behavior of butterflies seems casual and haphazard, no one is inclined to use the epithet "busy butterfly," yet lepidoptera are next in importance to bees as pollinators.

The image of the butterfly as a gourmet, sipping nectar from only the choicest of blossoms, is somewhat exaggerated. Sweets in general attract many species. The spring sap from a tapped or storm-damaged sugar maple has excellent drawing power. Various species of anglewings, venturing from hibernation on a warm spring day, line up and feed avidly. After dark the same tree becomes clothed with hundreds of feeding moths, especially sallows (*Eupsilia*) and pinions (*Lithophane*). Later in the year, fallen fruit, particularly if it has begun to rot or ferment, also holds great attraction. Moths and butterflies enjoying this fare become docile and inebriated, making photography particularly easy. The inevitable hornets that share the banquet are a limited hazard, as they, too, are usually tipsy and not defensive.

The gourmet image is totally shattered when you chance upon a toad crushed in the road. Such an unfortunate individual, if adequately rotted, may be obscured by a cluster of feeding butterflies, particularly anglewings, red-spotted purples, swallowtails, and even the dainty blues. The species of animal is of no consequence. If it has decomposed to the point that the butterflies (or moths) can sip solutions of liquefied proteins or amino acids, it seems to be irresistible. In a study of pig carrion in South Carolina, where twenty-one species of butterflies and moths were recorded, it was noted that the traffic was heaviest when the stench of decay was at its height.

Once, on a trip to Ecuador, we lost track of a lepidopterist friend for an entire day, only to learn that he had been ensconced in a pasture in the blazing tropical sun, reveling in the host of butterflies banqueting on the reeking carcass of a cow. Lepidopterists are a dedicated lot, but fortunately that kind of lep-watching is optional!

To shatter the gourmet label more completely, one need only contemplate the delicate spring azure sipping from chickadee droppings beneath the bird feeder, or watch the elegant banded purples, in rich, formal attire, shouldering each other aside on bear dung in the forests of Maine. Feces, fresh or stale, are almost as irresistible to some lepidoptera as is carrion. Fecal matter, as a natural part of the biosphere, is exploited by many insects, and if you want to go where the butterflies are, it is necessary to suppress the natural tendency to avoid it (fig. 8–2).

One of the most productive nonfloral sites for butterfly watching is at patches of wet sand, soil, or mud around puddles, along stream margins, or at bankside seeps. Here you will often find butterflies in groups of two or three, or by the hundreds, drinking from the moist ground. There may be but a single species or many species all together. They will be almost entirely males and, inevitably, the term "puddle club" has been commonly applied to such congregations. They may be quite tolerant of your close approach, then suddenly fly up en masse and disperse, only to return one by one and reassemble on the same patch.

What is the attraction? When you chance upon a puddle in your wanderings, it is rarely possible to know its history. Is it merely rainwater in an otherwise barren wheel rut, or has the

Figure 8–2 Silvery checkerspots (*Chlosyne nycteis*) feeding

Figure 8–3 Silver spotted skipper (*Epargyreus clarus*) and eastern tailed blues (*Everes comyntas*) "puddling"

water been enriched by substances that the butterflies need and seek out? Butterflies, like all other organisms, certainly need to replenish their water supplies, and they have need for various salts, but there must be more to it than that. One edge of a puddle frequently gets all the action, while the other edges are deserted. A puddle in a barnyard can be highly attractive, while one in a plowed field may not be. Moist patches in the ashes of an extinguished campfire are very popular. The common denominator is most likely organic matter containing amino acids from urine and feces. In the case of the ashes, the answer may be meat drippings, or urine used to put out the fire. Whatever the attraction, there is hardly a more dramatic butterfly spectacle than a well-patronized puddle club (fig. 8–3).

Most moths and butterflies feed by sipping up exposed liquids from flowers, secretions and excretions of plants and animals, and seepages from decaying fruit and animal bodies. A few species of moths have gone beyond this and have developed the ability to pierce intact skin with a specially adapted proboscis. The colorful herald moth (*Scoliopteryx libatrix*), found throughout the Northern Hemisphere, can pierce the skin of sound fruit with its spined tongue to drink the juices inside. And the ultimate has been accomplished by a Malaysian moth, a cousin of the Canadian calpe (*Calpe canadensis*). It has developed the ability to pierce the intact skin of cattle and other animals and to suck blood in a manner any mosquito would envy. But fear not: *Calpe eustrigata*, as this threatening moth is called, is not present in North America to compete with our black flies, deer flies, and green-heads!

Since feeding is such a basic activity of moths and butterflies, it would seem that knowing where and when they feed would be all that is necessary to locate particular species. While it is helpful, this is only partly true. Some moths, having no digestive tracts as adults, never feed and can be located only by searching them out while at rest (usually a serendipitous achievement) or by taking advantage of their mating activities or their attraction to light.

TEMPERATURE CONTROL

Lepidoptera are cold-blooded; the temperature of their bodies is determined largely by their environment. In order for them to fly, their flight muscles must be warmed to a temperature that allows them to contract vigorously and rapidly. Too little heat makes flight impossible, and too much heat can be damaging. Much butterfly behavior is directed toward temperature control, and this, in turn affects our opportunities for lepwatching.

When the air is cool—whether it be early in the season, early in the morning, on an "in and out," partly sunny day, or at high altitude or high latitude—butterflies need to warm up before they can fly. Often they will walk to a sunny spot, or wait until a patch of sunlight reaches them, then spread their wings broadly, with back to the sun, so that the sun's rays will strike the wings and body perpendicularly (fig. 8–4). Butterflies living in the arctic or on high mountains, where they must warm up for every flight, often have the bases of the wings covered with black or very dark scales. The body seems to be set in the middle of a black

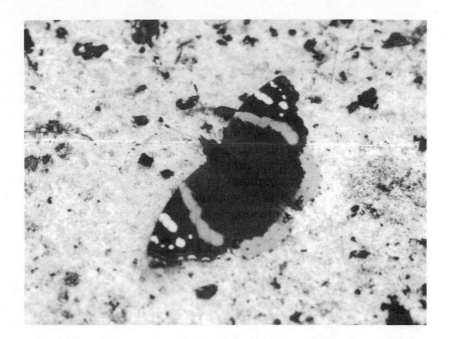

Figure 8–4 Red admiral (*Vanessa atalanta*), dorsal basking

coin. Sunlight striking this area warms the body enough so that the butterfly can take off. In cold climates, the insects fly only while the sun is shining. When a cloud intervenes, the butterfly drops to the ground and folds its wings over its back, becoming very inconspicuous. When the sunshine returns, it spreads its wings to bask, and soon is ready to fly again. The sulphur butterflies sit with their wings folded over the back and do "lateral basking": they turn sideways to the sun, leaning so that the sun's rays strike the wings perpendicularly. The more northern sulphurs have increased black scaling on the undersurface of the wings, speeding the warming process. Many butterflies alight on the sunny side of dark-colored rocks and tree trunks so that they can be warmed from both sides at once. Basking sites offer excellent opportunities for close observation.

In cool climates, the passage of a cloud over the sun can put an abrupt end to flying; in the Mexican canyons where the monarch butterflies overwinter, quite a different sort of behavior occurs.

In spring, when the butterflies are readying themselves for the flight north, they spend a great deal of time basking in the sun, raising body temperature. If a cloud obscures the sun, the basking butterflies take to the wing en masse and circle about, maintaining heat by using their flight muscles. When the sun returns, they promptly settle down and resume basking. While this activity consumes energy, they can afford it. At this season there are many flowers blooming, and the butterflies spend part of each day feeding. The spectacle of the cloudy sky being further darkened by a cloud of butterflies when the sun is obscured is almost unbelievable.

Because nocturnal moths cannot use sunlight for passive warming, they must resort to muscular activity in order to prepare to fly. Just as we warm up by shivering, they vibrate their wings rapidly to raise muscle temperature. If a recently emerged moth you are watching begins to quiver its wings rapidly, beware. It is about to bid you good-bye! This vibrating activity is common in large and heavy-bodied moths, but small moths and those with slender bodies seem to have muscles that can function through a wide range of temperatures. Micro moths, when the temperature is 35°F, can spring into flight just as quickly as when the weather is warm.

If raising the body temperature is important, keeping it down is equally so. On hot, sunny days, many butterflies that normally rest with wings outspread close their wings over their backs when they alight. They even rest so that the sun strikes them directly from the front or rear, with the wings parallel to the sun's rays. In this position not only do they pick up little heat from the sun, but they also cast a very thin shadow and are less visible to predators. Sometimes on hot days all the members of a puddle club will be lined up at the same angle.

MATING AREAS AND BEHAVIOR

While feeding and temperature control are basic activities for most adult insects, their purpose is to make mating and subsequent egg laying possible. Seeking out mates can be a very energetic activity for one or both sexes. If you know something of butterfly behavior when they are engaged in this pursuit (and pursuit it often is!), your opportunities for observation will be greatly improved. Photography is another matter. Keeping butterflies in focus during their courtship routines can be a bit of a trick.

Searching activities by males—flying back and forth in a seemingly haphazard fashion over areas where females may be emerging or feeding—is a method of mate location used by many butterflies. When a potential mate is sighted, the male may then initiate his courtship routine. There are almost as many forms of courtship as there are species of butterflies. Many still await careful observation and recording.

In some species, including many of the swallowtails, this searching is more organized and is called "patrolling." The male lays out a more or less circular route that he traverses again and again, usually in the same direction, often taking ten to fifteen minutes to make one round trip. We have clocked a tiger swallowtail (*Papilio glaucus*) on such a patrol, and his time varied by no more than one to two minutes per cycle. If he encounters another male along the way, a dog fight ensues and the intruder is usually driven off. If a female is encountered, he will try to induce her to mate. Both searching and patrolling activities consume a significant amount of energy.

A less costly approach is "perching," practiced by many smaller butterflies, such as some hairstreaks and the dusky wing skippers. The male selects an elevated perch, on a branch tip or tall weed, where he has an unobstructed view of a surrounding territory a number of yards in diameter. When an insect about his own size enters the territory, he dashes out to investigate. If it is a different species, he quickly returns to his perch. If it is another male, the two engage in combat that often consists of an upward-spiraling flight for as much as several hundred feet. The intruder usually breaks away and departs, and the first male descends to his perch. A passing female, on the other hand, is intercepted in a more gentlemanly fashion, and courtship is initiated.

In some parts of the country, particularly in the more open areas of the West and Southwest, both sexes of some species engage in *hilltopping*. They fly to a small hill or knoll, where the males patrol in search of females. In such situations, male swallowtails have been observed to attack one another with such violence that both sustained severe wing damage. Many times such hilltops have no flowers suitable for nectaring, and no growth of larvel food plants. The butterflies seem to be there solely for the purpose of finding mates. With considerable numbers of a species thus concentrated in one place, the chances for successful mating are increased.

Because of their nocturnal habits, the mating activities of moths have been less frequently observed. In many instances, visual search by males has been replaced by chemical attraction, and here the female takes the initiative. The female moth, after emergence and before flying, sits and disperses a chemical scent

(pheromone) from glands at the end of the abdomen. The male moth detects single molecules of this scent with sensory hairs on its antennae and follows them upwind to find and mate with the female. You can observe this most readily with a few common species of day-flying moths. Those male gypsy moths (*Lymnatria dispar*) careening crazily about your yard or woods are hot on the scent, but it is rather difficult to follow them to their quarry. A freshly emerged female promethea moth (*Callosamia promethea*), protected by a screened cage and set outdoors in the early afternoon, may soon attract several dozen great black males, all assembling from downwind. And a caged virgin female buck moth (*Hemileuca lucina*), set out in late morning in a site where the species is plentiful, will be totally engulfed by a buzzing mass of hundreds of black, white, and red males within a few minutes (fig. 8–5). The competition for

Figure 8–5 Male New England buck moths (*Hemileuca lucina*) attracted to a caged, calling female

mates is indeed intense. These are scenes where motion photography is particularly rewarding.

Mating in lepidoptera, once initiated, is a rather leisurely process that may continue for one to several hours with many butterflies, and from the middle of the night through the following afternoon in the larger silkmoths. Moths tend to remain completely at rest and in a concealed situation until mating is finished, but some butterflies will fly about while copulating, particularly if they feel threatened by your close approach. In some species, the female does the flying and the male remains passive with wings folded over the back; in other species, the reverse is the case. If you can approach a mating pair without spooking it, as you frequently can, it is very easy to take good photographs (fig. 8–6).

Capturing a mating pair in order to obtain eggs for rearing has its drawbacks and its advantages. Often the pair will break off before fertilization has been accomplished, and the yield will be infertile eggs or none at all. On the other hand, if mating does proceed to completion without interruption, you have the advantage of knowing just what the male parent was like. This is of great interest in species with variable color forms. It makes it possible to learn about the inheritance of the various colors and patterns.

Figure 8–6 Mating pair of inornate ringlets (*Coenonympha inornata*)

LARVAL FOOD PLANT

Important as are these details in locating a particular species of moth or butterfly, the presence of the larval food plant is still the most significant. The caterpillar does not wander very far away from the food plant before pupating, and the fertilized female cannot do her part in continuing the species if a suitable larval food plant is not available. The food plant may be present without the moth or butterfly, but if the moth or butterfly is a resident species that is reproducing, the food plant must be there. Thus you can often locate a butterfly most easily by locating its larval food plant: for a hackberry butterfly (*Asterocampa celtis*), you need hackberry trees; for a bog copper (*Epidemia epixanthe*), you need cranberry.

There are always exceptions. Some moths and butterflies, in response to rapid increases in population and assisted by prevailing winds, will disperse hundreds or even over a thousand miles from the nearest area where a suitable food plant grows. You may see pink-spotted hawk-moths (*Agrius cingulatus*) along the New England coast far from any sweet potato vines or pawpaw, or the black witch (*Ascalapha odorata*) in Maine or Minnesota a thousand miles from the nearest acacia. But these are dead-end situations; the moths cannot reproduce in these far-off areas. Seeing such moths is a matter of chance. They cannot be specifically sought out.

CHAPTER 9

Food Plant Specificity

Figure 9–1 Black swallowtail larva
(*Papilio polyxenes*)

Plants are not just a mixture of nutrients. Along with carbohydrates, proteins, and fats, they are laced with chemicals that defend them against hungry caterpillars or that the caterpillar may use to its own advantage. Each caterpillar has a specific menu that it can digest and on which it can thrive, and it or its egg-laying parent is attracted to the plant or plants on this menu. Isolate a caterpillar with an unsuitable food plant and it will starve, or it will feed, sicken, and die. "One larva's salad is another one's poison," so to speak.

For some species of caterpillar, the menu is limited to a single species of plant, or to a few closely related species in the same genus. The American copper butterfly (*Lycaena phlaeas americana*) chooses sheep sorrell. The large fritillaries (genus *Speyeria*) need violets. Milbert's tortoise (*Aglais milberti*) requires nettles. Larvae of many of the borer moths (genus *Papaipema*) feed in the roots of but a single plant species: ironweed (for *P. cerrusata*), Joe-Pye weed (*P. eupatorii*), sensitive fern (*P. inquaesita*), and bracken (*P. pterisii*), to name a few.

Many species are able to thrive on a number of closely related plants. The waved sphinx caterpillar (*Ceratomia undulosa*) eating ash in the wild may do equally well on lilac or privet from your yard. Apple is often an adequate substitute for cherry or plum. Most of the willow feeders are happy with aspen and poplar (but not with tulip poplar, which is not a poplar!). Hickory can often be interchanged with butternut or black walnut, although some hickory-feeding underwing moths seem partial to a single species.

Sometimes a species with limited preference when young will accept other species as it gets older. The Baltimore checkerspot (*Euphydryas phaeton*) regularly lays its eggs on white turtlehead, and the young larvae remain with that plant until they hibernate. However, in the spring, the maturing larvae will also eat penstemmon if it is within reasonable walking distance (which can be many yards, even for very small caterpillars). Eggs and young larvae of the buck moth (*Hemileuca maia*) are normally found on small scrubby oaks, but as they grow older they are often seen feeding successfully on cherry and other unrelated plants. Many of the species that may shift food plants when older are colonial feeders. Their eggs are laid in large clusters on the original food plant, and the caterpillars feed side by side as they grow. When the original plant is stripped, they move off in search of more food, sometimes en masse if a similar plant is close by, or in smaller groups or singly to other plant species. We have seen mourning cloak (*Nymphalis antiopa*) larvae leave a stripped willow and finish feeding on burr reed (*Sparganum*), a totally unrelated plant.

Leafing through field guides to learn of food plants, you often see the term *general feeder*. Such species are rather goatlike in their ability to thrive on a great variety of trees and shrubs; many noctuid and geometrid moth larvae can do this. Another common designation is *low plants*, especially for arctiid moths. Such species are happy with dandelion, plantain, wild lettuce, and a great variety of other flowering plants. If you are rearing such larvae late in the season, any type of grocery store lettuce (the greener the better) is a useful substitute.

A word is in order here about field guides and other reference books. They can at times be weak on the subject of larval food plants. This is not the fault of their authors. No one can have had personal experience with all the known food plants of all the species in all parts of the country. Many food plant listings are necessarily obtained from other publications. If a writer of one hundred years ago, esteemed in his time and in ours, made an error in citing a food plant, that error may continue to be quoted. Perhaps he had observed something not witnessed recently. More probably he was watching a different species, subsequently defined as distinct, rather than the one he was familiar with. Samuel Scudder described several of the dusky wing skippers before 1875, but he was unaware of another species, the wild indigo dusky wing, described in 1936 and common in the parts of New England he frequented. This species was responsible for some of his observations that are now considered to be incorrect. Other food plant records have come from people whose knowledge of botany was limited. Yet once such a statement is in print, no author feels quite comfortable in discarding it. After all, some of the most unlikely things actually happen— witness our mourning cloaks eating burr reed.

Another source of confusion can be biological. A food plant that may seem illogical to an observer in one part of the country, in terms of his own experience, may turn out to be the only food plant accepted somewhere else. Unexpected may not be wrong.

As a practical matter, lep-watchers need to use the books as guides, to try to identify correctly the insects and plants being observed, and to record the observations for future reference. It takes only one fact to puncture a fallacy, and amateur naturalists have punctured many hundreds. In this book we have attempted to draw upon our own experiences whenever possible, but it will not surprise us if we have made statements that our readers will happily refute.

CHAPTER
10

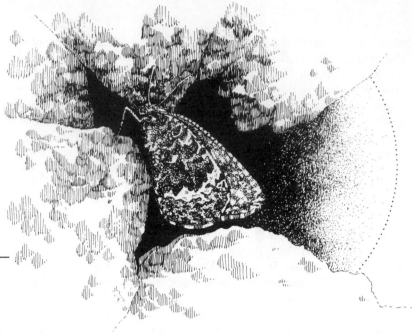

Habitat

Figure 10–1 White Mountain butterfly (*Oeneis melissa semidea*)

Habitat means the kind of place in which a particular animal or plant naturally lives or grows. In the case of moths and butterflies, the habitat is determined by the climate—the distribution of light, warmth, humidity, and air movement throughout the year—the underlying soil, and the plants that the climate and soil foster. For a particular species, the habitat is made up of places where the larval food plant grows, places where flowers and other feeding sources are available, and locations where mating activities take place. For some, all these resources are in the same place. Sulphur butterflies take nectar from meadow flowers among which they find clover plants for egg laying; the males patrol those same meadows in search of mates. Tiger swallowtails and red spotted purples seek mates and lay eggs in the wooded areas where the larval food plants grow, but they regularly come out

into nearby fields and roadsides to nectar at flowers. Some butterflies—many swallowtails, some fritillaries, and some elfins and hairstreaks, to name a few—engage in hilltopping as a major element in their mating activities. Hence their habitats may include areas devoid of their nectaring and larval food plants, and often quite distant from them.

Old fields, meadows, and power line cuts are favorite sites for lep-watchers. Here many species may be found together. In the drier, upland situations, one commonly finds coppers, ringlets, wood nymphs, painted ladies, and crescents. In lower, moist situations, there are at least skippers, meadow fritillaries, and Baltimore checkerspots. Tiger moths may be flushed by your passing, or found roosting beneath leaves. At night, looper moths (plusiines) and sphinx moths hover at flowers, nectaring. During the day the swallowtails patrol at wood edges or bask in the sun with admiral butterflies. Deeper in the woods, especially along paths and around clearings, are the pearly eye and anglewings. In swampy woods, the Appalachian eyed brown (*Satyrodes appalachia*) appears, often but a few yards away from a sunny swale where the northern eyed brown (*S. eurydice*) is flying. These two butterflies are very similar, differing only in markings beneath the hind wing, and in their habitats.

Some butterflies have very limited habitats. The rare skipper (*Problema bulenta*) was so named because for nearly a century after it was discovered, no one was able to find it again. It was rediscovered near Wilmington, North Carolina, and has since been found in many places from Georgia to Maryland, in rather inaccessible brackish marshes near estuaries. The rare skipper turns out to be a common skipper in an uncommon habitat rarely frequented by lep-watchers. It has recently been reported nectaring by the hundreds at buttonbush blossoms at the edges of these marshes.

Another very limited habitat is that of the eastern pigmy blue (*Brephidium pseudofea*), which lives in the narrow band of glasswort at the margins of tidal flats along the southeastern coast of the United States. The only easy way to find the butterfly is to locate the habitat and look for an inconspicuous brown butterfly, a little over ½″ broad, flying close to the ground. Once seen, it is very easy to observe. Because of its minute size, a trip of a few yards is a major excursion. Finding the larvae is another matter. They are green like the glasswort and feed within a pinhole they drill into the stem, leaving nothing but their posteriors exposed.

Bogs are a kind of habitat irresistible to lep-watchers. Many bogs are relict bits of wetland left behind as the last glacier receded. They are habitats matched only by tundra areas hundreds of miles farther north. The plant and insect groups they support have in some instances been isolated long enough to have evolved into distinct subspecies. Several species of lesser fritillaries and arctics, widespread inhabitants of Canadian tundra, are found in acid bogs in the northeastern United States. The black spruce that is usually present is not a food plant for any of their larvae but serves as a marker for recognizing the right sort of bog. A colony of the western pine elfin (*Incisalia eryphon*) was recently discovered in such a bog in western Maine, nearly one thousand miles east of its nearest known distribution, in Michigan's Upper Peninsula.

Bogs, however, and particularly quaking bogs, have their hazards. They often contain one or more areas where the matted vegetation becomes thinner and more grassy—the "eye" of the bog—where the footing is poor but the swimming is better. A learned entomologist friend of ours once disappeared, temporarily, into the eye of a bog when he was paying more attention to entomology than to botany! Working in pairs is a good practice for bog-watching bug-watchers.

Another productive habitat type is the pine barren. Clad in a cover of pitch pine, scrub oak, and blueberries, barrens are of little value for timber or agriculture, but vulnerable as cheap real estate for conversion into industrial sites. The plant communities they support often contain species from much farther south or north. They are the home of lepidoptera, particularly moths, not found in adjacent fields and forests. These species come readily to bait or light.

Most butterflies remain in a single habitat throughout the year. The mon-

Figure 10–2 Clusters of monarch butterflies (*Danaus plexippus*) roosting on fir trees in Michoacan, Mexico

arch (*Danaus plexippus*), however, changes its habitat with the season. During the warm months, its reproductive period, it frequents open spaces, fields, and roadsides where milkweed grows. In autumn the butterflies stop reproducing and concentrate in areas where they can feed on the nectar of late-blooming flowers, especially asters and goldenrods, storing up fat to fuel their long migration to eucalyptus groves on the California coastline, or to stands of fir in high-altitude canyons in the Transvolcanic Range of southwestern Mexico (fig. 10–2). In these overwintering sites they require fairly stable temperatures just above freezing, protection from drying winds, and available drinking water. Since no single temperate zone location can supply all three of these needs, the fundamentally tropical monarch butterfly must move up and down the continent with the changing seasons. This two-way, seasonal migration is unique.

You may sometimes find that a habitat, apparently just right for a particular species, is unoccupied. Misjudging the butterfly's flight season is one reason for disappointment. The insect may be there, but not in a stage of development that can easily be detected. In other instances, the habitat is truly empty, perhaps because the range of the species you seek has been shrinking over the recent past. This is the case with the regal fritillary (*Speyeria idalia*) and the imperial moth (*Eacles imperialis*) in the Northeast. For some species, a patch of appropriate habitat may be simply too small. A female buck moth (*Hemileuca maia*), exploring quite widely before selecting a place for her eggs, may fly off a site of only a few acres of pine barren and end up laying her eggs in an unsatisfactory spot. But the delicate and close-ranging Karner blue butterfly (*Lycaeides melissa samuelis*), which occupies the same type of habitat, can thrive on an acre or two.

A habitat may be empty because of a catastrophe that wiped out previous occupants. A fire will usually destroy only part of a pine or blueberry barren, and the population will soon be restored from the unburned areas. Following a severe and total burning, it may be years before a wandering female recolonizes the site. Some sites, relict bogs in particular, may be so remote from any occupied similar habitat that recolonization never occurs. Similarly, flooding can depopulate an area. A locality in central

Maine famous for a subspecies of the Dorcas copper (*Lycaena dorcas*) was submerged by a beaver dam. When the beavers left after many years, the butterflies returned.

More devastating, and of greater concern, is the hand of man and his chemicals. Widespread spraying against a "nuisance" insect can wipe out a fragile species with specialized habitat requirements. Recolonization of the contaminated habitat may be difficult or very delayed. Lowering the level of ground water by pumping can destroy an essential food plant, and thus a butterfly population can be wiped out.

On the other hand, changes in habitats may be natural and, in the balance, positive. Normal vegetational succession results in changes in the moths and butterflies that inhabit an area. An abandoned plowed field becomes a weed lot, and species move in that are partial to the assortment of annual plants that thrive there. In a few years, perennial grasses and wild flowers convert the site into an "old field," and another assortment of moths and butterflies becomes resident. As weed trees begin to seed into the old field and flourish, gradually converting it into a wood, still other species come to predominate. After many decades, the mature forest of more durable trees hosts an assortment of lepidoptera unknown in the weed lot.

The author of one regional guide to butterflies (Arthur M. Shapiro in *Butterflies of the Delaware Valley*) stated in his introduction that he refused to pinpoint the locations of colonies of particular species of butterflies, so that traffic of trampling feet would not damage fragile habitats. He preferred instead to describe the characteristics of the habitat, leaving each lep-watcher to go out and discover his own site. Knowledge of the distribution of the species would be thereby enhanced. We strongly endorse this principle.

The triad of range, timing, and habitat forms the foundation for locating particular species of moths and butterflies. Develop an eye for habitat, and you will open up new horizons for lep-watching.

CHAPTER
11

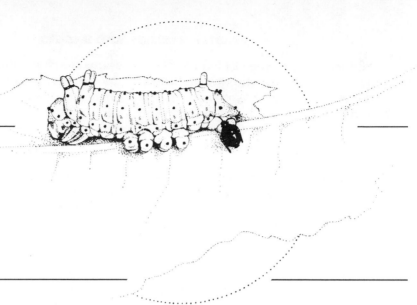

Hazards

Figure 11–1 Stinkbug feeding on promethea moth larva (*Callosamia promethea*)

When a flying moth or butterfly crosses your line of vision, you are looking at a real success story, a combination of significant strategies and plain good luck, but before the day is over the chances are great that one or another of the strategies will have failed or the luck run out. As with all organisms, the goal of life is to reproduce before the curtain falls, and lepidoptera are no exception. The female tries to tip the balance in her favor by laying many hundreds of eggs, but only 1 or 2 percent of these reach maturity, the rest falling victims of unfavorable weather, disease, parasites, and predators.

VERTEBRATES

Foremost among predators are birds. Without birds, many populations of lepidoptera would explode uncontrollably. But without lepidoptera, many species of birds could not survive.

Chickadees, nuthatches, and creepers search out the tiny eggs hidden by female moths in crevices of tree bark. Other species search for larvae. Warblers and orioles systematically examine twigs and branches, picking off caterpillars at a prodigious rate. The larvae boring within wood are beset by the woodpecker as it chips and chops to extract them from their burrows. Pupae buried in the leaf litter are safer from the inquisitive eyes of many birds, but the towhee scratching through the fallen leaves uncovers and destroys a great many. And even the pupae within the tough cocoons of the silk moths are not secure; woodpeckers often puncture and raid these bastions.

The ability to fly does not give butterflies and moths the advantage that might be imagined, since they come up against those aerial specialists, the swifts, swallows, and flycatchers, not to mention the more conventional birds, which try to snatch them out of the air whenever the opportunity presents. One day I watched a hairstreak, which had just eluded my net, disappear with the "snap!" of a swallow's bill. And while writing this chapter, we watched a pair of phoebes feeding their four fledglings. Every minute or two, one parent or the other returned to the nest, its beak filled with moths.

Butterflies and moths are at risk not only while flying. Birds seek them out in their daytime resting places, or snatch them as they are feeding. It is not unusual to see the margins of a succulent puddle garnished with the severed wings of butterflies.

But the bird is not always the winner. If you find you have captured a moth or butterfly with V-shaped markings on its wings, or even with a triangular piece of wing missing completely, do not be disappointed. Such defects were caused by an attacking bird that tried and failed. As you study marks of this sort, you will be able to recreate a picture of what the insect was doing at the time of the attack. A triangular beak mark or piece of membrane loss on a single wing usually means that the insect was in flight when attacked and managed to tear itself loose.

Many moths rest on flat surfaces, such as tree trunks, with the forewings overlapping and completely covering the hind wings. A moth grasped by a bird's beak while in this position may show damage to both the upper and lower wings on one side of the body. Other moths and many butterflies rest with the wings folded together over the back, with hind wings overlapping forewings. An attack in this instance may leave paired marks on wings on both sides of the body.

Other vertebrates share in the destruction of lepidoptera. In the warmer climates, lizards add considerably to the toll. The moth or butterfly with a trapezoidal, rather than a triangular, mark of damage on its wings is likely to have escaped from a lizard. Shrews and small rodents search out and destroy hidden pupae, and at night the bats take over for the birds, snaring moths in midflight.

In a limited way, even humans are true predators on lepidoptera, in the sense that they occasionally use them as food. Pupae of a buck moth (*Coloradia pandora lindseyi*), whose larval food plant is ponderosa pine, used to be gathered in large numbers by the Piute Indians of northern California, who would roast them and eat them as a great delicacy. And the larva of a giant skipper (genus *Agathymus*) that feeds in the manguey plant and could have become a magnificent gold-and-black skipper, ends up as the "agave worm" in the tequila bottle.

INSECTS AND SPIDERS

Invertebrate predators, although not as obvious at first, are major participants in the lepidopteran smorgasbord. Many species of wasps paralyze and carry home small caterpillars with which they stock their cells, as food for their own offspring. Recently I lifted a T-square down from the wall over my workbench, rupturing on earthen cell that a wasp had constructed behind it. Out fell nine small microlepidopteran larvae, wiggling feebly but unable to crawl, fresh meat for a soon-to-hatch wasp larva.

Other wasps and hornets are strictly butchers. Yellow jackets attack a feeding caterpillar and, without even stinging it, use their mandibles to carve it into chunks to be carried back to the nest. We have had white faced hornets invade our bait traps, attack a resting red admiral or large underwing moth, chop off the wings one by one, and hack the body into manageable portions. They then chewed a hole through the trap wall and carried off their provisions, an indignity to beast and man alike!

There are aerial predators as well. Small moths and butterflies can be captured on the wing by robber flies. Even a large buck moth, in its bulletlike flight above a scrub oak thicket, can be snatched from the air by a patrolling dragon fly.

We witnessed just such a scene one April while walking along a wooded path on the Island of Ossabaw in Georgia. A large satyrid butterfly was making its crooked way down the path toward us when suddenly an even larger dragon fly darted out of the woods like an emerald arrow. It snatched the butterfly in midair and sped into the thick underbrush on the opposite side of the path. What a picture! We started to follow it, but pursuit was just about hopeless, thrashing about, as we were, in a virtual quagmire. Every time we managed to work close enough to lift camera to eye, the dragon fly moved, and each time, half of the problem was to find the uncooperative creature as it darted among the leaves and twigs to a new, farther-away, and better-camouflaged situation. It continued to munch on the butterfly. Eventually we gave up the chase and continued on our walk. On the way back, we found the wings strewn on the path. It was a pearly eye (*Enodia portlandia*).

Other insects take a tremendous toll of larval and mature lepidoptera. Stinkbugs search through the foliage, stabbing and quickly immobilizing unsuspecting caterpillars with their stilettolike probosces. They then sit there, dissolving the interior organs with injected enzymes and sucking them out, as through a straw. In our own garden, where we have planted various flowers for the benefit of local butterflies, there was a stand of pearly everlasting inhabited by several caterpillars of the American painted lady (*Vanessa virginiensis*), which we had been monitoring daily. One by one they had been disappearing, until finally only one had survived long enough to reach its fifth and final instar. The next day I found it dead, and on an adjacent leaf sat a stinkbug, cleaning its beak with its front feet.

Our garden is full of such disasters. One year we happened upon a full-grown promethea caterpillar that had been feeding on wild cherry. A stinkbug had attacked it from behind, speared it, and was feeding on its inner juices (fig. 11–1). Either the caterpillar had been immobilized by the bug or it did not know it had been attacked, for it made no attempt to fight back.

Ambush bugs, another group of the true bugs, lurk motionless on flowers, awaiting the arrival of a nectaring insect. The speed with which they can attack and immobilize their prey is unbelievable. We once watched a cabbage butterfly alight on a yellow blossom. Instantly it bent its wings sharply downward, into a position unnatural for perching, and it never moved again. Closer inspection showed that it had been skewered by an ambush bug.

One day, while lep-watching in Colo-

Figure 11–2 Snowberry clearwing (*Hemaris diffinis*) captured by ambush bug (*Phymata fasciata*)

rado, we noticed a snowberry clearwing (*Hemaris diffinis*) apparently perching on an alfalfa blossom, in striking contrast to the expected behavior of hovering while feeding. When we looked more closely, we saw that the moth was not perching but had been captured and killed by an ambush bug a fraction of its weight, which had speared it as it hovered. The bug was desperately clinging to one frail alfalfa blossom, struggling to support the weight of the dead sphinx moth (fig. 11–2).

The prey does not always outweigh the hunter. One September we were out in the field with net and camera but had found very few lepidoptera of interest, until we happened upon a perfect, newly emerged black swallowtail (*Papilio polyxenes*), basking with open wings upon a small shrub. With cameras primed, we crept closer, and still the butterfly did not move. We were hardly more than a foot away when suddenly the plant's green stems were transformed into an enormous praying mantis (fig. 11–3). The head of the butterfly had already been eaten, and all too soon the wings, like those of the satyrid in Georgia, lay like confetti on the ground where we stood.

Beetles, while less dramatic, consume large numbers of caterpillars. Carabid

Figure 11–3 Black swallowtail (*Papilio polyxenes*) captured by praying mantis (*Tenodera sinensis*)

Figure 11–4 Wood nymph (*Cercyonis pegala alope*) captured by flower spider (genus *Misumena*)

beetles, especially the "caterpillar hunters," are large in size and in appetite. The tiger beetles (cicindelids) live up to their name. Both groups are predatory in the larval and in the adult stages.

So many times we have seen butterflies perching on meadow flowers enjoying a peaceful "happy hour," or just resting in the sun, seemingly waiting to be photographed. At such time, the photographer approaches with the greatest caution—marveling at the stillness of the subject, approaching so slowly, wondering that the butterfly can be oblivious of the observer's presence. And so many times it turns out that the little creature has literally been "stopped dead in its tracks" by a flower spider (*Misumena misumenops*). These little arachnids are so beautiful that it is hard to equate them with the art of sudden death. They hide their delicate pink-and-white or pink-and-yellow bodies among the petals of flowers so perfectly that one does not see that they are there—until a finger reaches to touch the butterfly. Then the spider moves. For some butterfly watchers, these small victims are the only butterflies they collect—these, and the victims of other insects (fig. 11–4).

Argiope aurantia, the famous garden spider, is at its best in an unmowed meadow, where it can anchor its web on the stems of all sorts of wild flowers and weeds. In the early morning, the web is quivering with dew drops, and sparkling. At the center the spider sits, motionless, its handsome black-and-yellow body at the middle of the ladder of silk that is its trademark, its black legs spread out like an evil star—a warning. A small yellow butterfly flutters up in response to the rising sun. Perhaps it did not see the web. Perhaps it was curious. Its feet, its wings, its body smash into the fabric of the web—and suddenly its life is over. In a fraction of a second, the spider has darted from its perch and begun to wrap the butterfly in a silken shroud that pours from glands in its abdomen. It rolls its victim over and over until it is locked in a tough shell of silk—a mummy case —to be stored until the spider chooses to penetrate it and dine on its inner juices (fig. 11–5).

Several days later in the summer, an even stranger event took place. While walking in the meadow, we came upon the web of a shamrock spider (*Araneus trifolia*). Next to the path there was a

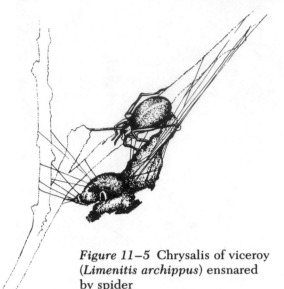

Figure 11–5 Chrysalis of viceroy (*Limenitis archippus*) ensnared by spider

very small willow tree, perhaps three feet tall, with little new leaves shooting out from its branchlets, all very new and fresh. On the top of the little tree, the spider had spun a bit of web and attached it to a larger tree. The rest of the web was anchored in several places, still quite close to the willow. The web, we could see, was finished and billowing slightly in the breeze. Just above the willow tree—in fact, barely touching it—was a little shelter made of leaves and silk. The spider crouched in it, watching and waiting.

At the bottom of the spindly little tree's trunk, we suddenly saw a bright green caterpillar of either a viceroy or a banded purple—we couldn't be sure which. It was eating leaves as it went. Before long, the spider noticed this also, and from time to time, she came partly out of her shelter to see what was happening. Each time the caterpillar finished a leaf, it crept up to the next one, coming closer to the spider with each move. The caterpillar did not see her, but she saw it. As each leaf was eaten, the caterpillar crawled up to the next, one pair of little hooked pads at a time, in sinuous sequence. With each new ascent the spider became more agitated. She seemed ready to pounce at any moment, but the caterpillar, in its slow and meticulous way, ate on, until there were only four of the little dagger-shaped leaves left on its side of the tree.

Finally it reached the place where the nest was attached to the willow, and as it chomped away, little waves were sent into the nest.

The spider sprang forth, dashed out into the middle of the web, and stood shaking it, making short forays in the caterpillar's direction from time to time, to which the caterpillar showed no concern whatsoever. It finished all the leaves on that side of the tree, ate off the apical bud, turned around and started back down, eating the few remaining leaves on the other side as it went, with classic unconcern. Having denuded the tree, it left it and walked away into the grasses. The spider returned to her nest.

PARASITES

The most sinister of the attacks on lepidoptera come from the parasitic wasps and flies. These insects are more properly referred to as "parasitoids": a parasitoid consumes and destroys the body of its host, whereas a true parasite lives within or on the surface of its host, without causing life-threatening damage. But in the sense that these wasps and flies make their living within other organisms, they are often referred to, loosely, as parasites.

Trichogrammatid wasps, so tiny as to be easily overlooked, complete all their immature stages within a lepidopteran egg. If you happen upon a sphinx moth egg that doesn't look right—dull and mottled, rather than a homogeneous pearly green—enclose it in a very small, very clean glass vial and wait a week or two. You may soon see a number of tiny, dustlike wasps, less than a millimeter long, walking about on the inner surface of the vial. The parent of these wasps had inserted within the sphinx egg a single egg of her own, which developed into a dozen or more embryos and eventually into as many mature wasps. For the sphinx, it was an exercise in futility.

Most of the hornworm larvae in a tomato patch eventually become decorated with dozens of small white cocoons, attached on end to the caterpillar's skin. The caterpillar stops feeding and within a day or two shrivels and dies. A few days later, the tops of the cocoons are opened up, as by a cut from a knife, and from each emerges a small braconid wasp. Their eggs had been laid beneath the caterpillar's skin while it was still small, and the wasp larvae had been eating within it ever since, not damaging the host until their own feeding was completed. It is curious that a caterpillar that continues to feed and appear healthy until the braconids "abandon ship" should promptly die. We have seen only one exception to this, a luna larva that continued to feed and thrive after a brood of braconids emerged. About five days later, a second batch of braconids surfaced, and the caterpillar died. The parasites seem to have some means of sparing the host until their own needs have been met. Other species of braconids, after leaving the host, move a few inches away and pupate within a communal silk mass on an adjacent leaf.

Not infrequently, a larva or chrysalis for which you have been tenderly caring will fail to continue its development at the expected pace, and soon you notice

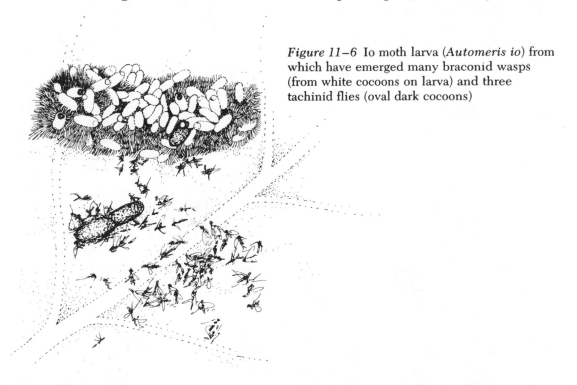

Figure 11–6 Io moth larva (*Automeris io*) from which have emerged many braconid wasps (from white cocoons on larva) and three tachinid flies (oval dark cocoons)

that an unusual wasp "has gotten into the cage." It may be large, brown, and peaceful, with a curved abdomen, or perhaps black, with antennae and legs banded with white and a habit of flicking its wings nervously. Your caterpillar may be a damp and shrunken remnant of its former self, or the chrysalis may be perforated with a neat round hole, just large enough for a wasp to climb out (fig. 11–7). Your charge has played host to an ichneumon wasp, whose egg was inserted into the caterpillar's body during one of its earlier instars.

Wasps are not the only villains. Flies also enter the act. The black swallowtail larva from the carrot row may sometimes be decorated with a few tiny, oval, white objects glued to the skin of its thorax. As you rear the caterpillar to maturity, it weakens and dies, and you discover a few capsule-shaped dark brown objects in the bottom of the cage. A tachinid fly has been at work, and the tiny white objects were its eggs. Its maggots bored through the caterpillar's skin, fed to maturity within the caterpillar, then chewed their way out again and formed the smooth brown pupa cases. They soon

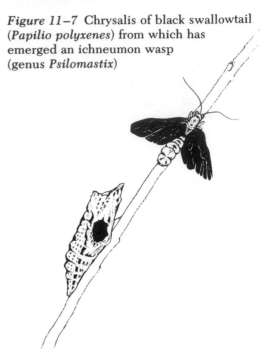

Figure 11–7 Chrysalis of black swallowtail (*Papilio polyxenes*) from which has emerged an ichneumon wasp (genus *Psilomastix*)

emerge as bristly black flies resembling houseflies.

Occasionally a single caterpillar will play host to a brood of braconids and several tachinids. They do not seem to have any problem sharing the same trough (fig. 11–6).

DISEASES

Caterpillars are often victims of bacterial and viral infections. These seem usually to be fatal, or at least we recognize only the fatalities. None of these diseases, fortunately, can be caught by humans.

When an outbreak of caterpillars suddenly "crashes," it is usually in large part the result of a widespread infection, rather than simply predation or control by parasites. Caterpillars that are malnourished as a result of complete defoliation of their food plants are more susceptible to viral infection. Following the last local gypsy moth outbreak, we

saw hundreds of dead larvae dangling from the undersides of oak branches, looking like so many wet socks. Those that survived and pupated apparently passed the virus along through their eggs. The following year, the larvae had ample food available but fed very slowly and died of the "wet sock disease" shortly before pupation. This infection is more properly called "wilt" disease and is caused by a polyhedral virus. *Bacillus thuringensis*, a bacterium sprayed for biological control of caterpillar outbreaks, has similar effects. While we may look upon these microbial diseases as fortunate when a pest species is out of hand, there are profound effects on other species of lepidoptera as well. Following the crash of a gypsy moth outbreak, there may be greatly reduced numbers of other species of moths and butterflies in the area, often for a period of several years.

PHYSICAL HAZARDS

For the lepidoptera that manage to avoid the predators, parasites, and diseases, the uncertainties of the physical environment add further risk. A cold and pelting spring rain can dislodge and drown many early instar larvae. An unseasonable frost may destroy the early spring vegetation on which the larvae depend or may terminate the growing season prematurely in autumn before larvae are fully grown. Drought may reduce the quality of foliage to a point where the caterpillar's size and vigor are impaired. Overheating is also a risk, particularly in artificial rearing situations. Caterpillars seem to deal with this effectively in the wild, by seeking shade when necessary.

MAN-MADE HAZARDS

As if all these natural hazards were not enough, the activities of humans are tipping the balance even further. Environmental contamination by pesticides is common. Many a thriving rearing project has been scuttled by uncontrolled aerial spraying. We do not yet know whether the general reduction of numbers of lepidoptera in the Northeast in the past few decades is in any way related to the increasing acidity of our rainfall. And specialized habitat destruction, locally in North America, and on a widespread basis throughout the tropics, has caused and will increasingly cause extinction of lepidopteran species. There are no refugee camps for butterflies.

Carefree as that butterfly may seem, the lot of a lep is not an easy one.

CHAPTER
12

Defenses

Figure 12–1 Pawpaw sphinx (*Dolba hyloeus*) on aspen trunk

For more than forty million years lepidoptera have been struggling for survival. The fossil record reveals a few details of the forms of some of the earliest species of moths and butterflies, but it tells nothing of the development of the defenses that have allowed them to evolve into the more than 115,000 species on the earth today. Most species can protect themselves enough to maintain fairly stable populations. The only hazards with which they are unable to deal effectively are those most recently introduced, by people.

CONCEALMENT

As with most animals, lepidoptera use concealment to avoid detection in all their stages. Underwing moths tuck eggs away in crevices in bark; the spring azure places hers singly among clusters of flower buds of similar size and color. The female American painted lady taps at the fuzzy surface of a pearly everlasting leaf with her diminutive front legs. Having found just the right spot, she curls her abdomen and deposits an egg beneath the fuzz, scarcely visible.

A few species don masquerade costumes. Larvae of emerald geometrine moths that feed on flowers will attach bits of flower petal to their backs, so that they seem to be a ragged piece of the blossom they are eating. The harvester larva, browsing upon woolly aphids, becomes so decorated with fluff from its victims as to be invisible. We once brought home a twig full of aphids as food for one harvester larva. The cluster of aphids contained six more larvae that we had been unable to see.

Many species hide. Underwing larvae,

especially as they become larger, climb down the food tree before dawn and lie quietly among vegetation on the ground until dark. Larvae of skippers, the spice bush swallowtail, and hibernating viceroys hide in leaf shelters constructed for the purpose. Pupating blues and hairstreaks commonly hide among the leaf litter to avoid detection, and great numbers of moth species do the same or even bury themselves deeply in the soil. Hibernating anglewing butterflies hide beneath any durable shelter: a loose shingle, the bark of a dead tree, a woodpile. American copper underwings (*Amphipyra pyramidoides*) hide in similar spots just for the day, often in groups of dozens or more. Concealment gives protection not only from predators but also from overheating during the day.

Encasing is another effective maneuver. The bagworm larva (*Thyridopterix ephaemeraeformis*) lives within a homemade sack constructed of fragments of vegetation from its food plant; it passes the major part of its life in the bag. The female even mates and lays her eggs without leaving the bag. But success is relative; from some bags only wasps emerge. The familiar cocoons of the cecropia, polyphemus, and other silk moths are elaborate examples of generally successful encasement.

CAMOUFLAGE

Probably the most widely used strategies for survival are camouflage, deception, and imitation.

Inchworms are particularly good at this. Some grasp a small twig with their only two pairs of prolegs and hold the body in a stiffly angled posture, with head and thoracic legs hunched together, looking like a terminal bud on a twig (fig. 12–2). The grape looper, which feeds also on Virginia creeper, has a body the diameter of a leaf stem, and about the same length and texture. It rests with the prolegs grasping the base of the stem and the thoracic legs resting on another stem or a leaf margin. It becomes visible only when you realize that leaves do not have branching stems or two stems (fig. 12–3)! This caterpillar has two color forms: green on green stems, and reddish on plants with reddish stems. The larvae of some species of prominents (notodontids) have lost the ability to grasp with the last pair of prolegs. These are drawn out into pointed or filamentous processes (fig. 12–4). This, together with bizarre humps, green-and-rust color patterns, and odd posturing, results in a caterpillar that is very difficult to distinguish from a blighted and tattered leaf margin. The illusion is so effective that if you do succeed in spotting one of these larvae, it is still easy to overlook others only a few inches away on adjacent leaves.

Although most lepidoptera in the pupal stage are carefully hidden away within a shelter or cocoon or in the ground, many butterfly chrysalids are less well concealed and must resort to camouflage in order to survive. The chrysalis of the orange-tip (*Falcapica midea*), tapered and pointed, juts out at an angle from a twig, and is easily mistaken for a thorn (fig. 12–5). The exquisite green chrysalis of the cloudless

Figure 12–2 Twiglike geometrid larva (*Nacophora quernaria*)

Figure 12–3 Lesser grapevine looper (*Eulithis diversilineata*) in cryptic resting position on Virginia creeper

Figure 12–4 Larva of a notodont (*Furcula cinerea*)

Figure 12–5 Thornlike pupa of orange-tip (*Falcapica midea*), showing silken "seat belt"

sulphur (*Phoebis sennae*) will readily pass for a partly unfolded young leaf. Many of the dangling nymphalid chrysalids have bizarre shapes like crumpled dead leaves (fig. 5–4).

Some moths use odd postures in order to resemble various sorts of vegetation. The lettered sphinx (*Deidamia inscripta*) rests with its brown wings folded downward but its abdomen curled upward, just another dead leaf. Some of the notodonts, particularly *Schizura*, rest with the body projecting at an angle of 30°–60°, head against a stick, wings furled about the abdomen. What you see seems to be the stub of a dead twig.

A very frequently used camouflage trick is to resemble a bird dropping. Many caterpillars do this expertly, particularly the early instars of some of the swallowtails (fig. 5–5, frames 3 and 4). The tufted bird-dropping moth (*Cerma cerintha*) and some microlepidoptera play the same game. Birds are not attracted to such objects, and humans read-

ily overlook them as well. As you become accustomed to the appearance of these imitators and skillful at spotting them, some of your most promising finds will turn out to be—bird droppings.

Many times we have been strolling along a dirt road or some woodland path, counting species, only to have a butterfly take off almost from under our feet and disappear before we could be sure what it was. A butterfly or moth is relatively secure against its chosen background. By waiting until the last moment, it can burst forth without danger of being caught. Many butterflies, while highly colorful above, are very drab beneath. The anglewings readily pass for dead leaves when their wings are folded over their backs (fig. 12–6). A sharp angle or small projection on the hind wing gives the illusion of a leaf stem. The goatweed butterfly (*Anaea andrea*) is similarly camouflaged. Sulphurs, when resting beneath a leaf, look much like a shaded, live leaf. Other butterflies merely have a

Figure 12–6 Cryptic undersurface of question sign butterfly (*Polygonia interrogationis*)

duller pattern beneath, perhaps with an intricate array of shades and lines, as in the red admiral (*Vanessa atalanta*). They are very hard to see when at rest in a shaded situation. In arctic and alpine habitats these dull underside patterns often resemble the lichen-covered rocks among which the butterflies hide, as is the case with the White Mountain butterfly (*Oeneis melissa semidea*, fig. 10–1).

A small group of satyrids in South America (genus *Cithaerias*) has a particularly effective strategy. These butterflies fly close to the ground in dimly lit rain forests. Instead of having scale patterns arranged to look like something else, they have wings that are almost completely devoid of scales. You see right through them! If you are following one and take your eyes off it for an instant, you are hard put to relocate it.

Moths are masters at the art of blending into the background. The myriad patterns of wavy lines and alternating shades of pale and dark closely resemble patterns of bark, rock, or lichens (fig. 3–1). The moths seem to have consider-

able skill at selecting resting places with which their own patterns will harmonize. They are not perfect at this. You will sometimes see a moth resting on a surface where it is as obvious as a postage stamp on a letter. Yet for each of these you will overlook dozens with barklike patterns that match the background almost perfectly, such as the white underwing on white birch or the Ilia underwing on oak. The green marvel (*Agriopodes fallax*) makes a perfect match for a lichen-covered tree trunk.

Camouflage is unquestionably one of the functions of larval decoration. Caterpillars go to great lengths to avoid the sharp eyes of birds. If the markings and clothing of the caterpillar make it look like anything but a long, cylindrical worm, or make it blend into its background, it can be almost impossible to see until it moves. Tapered green larvae of many of the skippers, pressed so closely against the midrib of a grass blade as to cast no shadow, are sometimes more easily located with the fingers than with the eyes (fig. 12–7). The larva of the large tolype (*Tolype vel-*

Figure 12–7 European skipper larva (*Thymelicus lineola*)

leda)—with its hair short on the back and longer and silky on the sides, dark gray and soft as the pelt of a mole, lying lengthwise on an apple twig—blends so well with the bark that it looks like nothing more than a slight thickening of the twig on which it rests. Its cocoon on the concave curve of the twig, fine gray hairs mixed in with the silk, continues the illusion.

Larval hairs retain usefulness even after pupation. Many species, while spinning a shelter, rub off the body hairs and incorporate them into the outside layers of the cocoon. They contribute to the color of the cocoon, often making it less apparent; they may also make the cocoon irritating enough to discourage eating by rodents. It is also possible that by weaving its bristly "overcoat" into the outer layers of the cocoon, the larva makes sure that the lining of the cocoon will be "clean," with no bristles to damage the soft, newly formed pupa.

Instead of trying to blend into the background, some larvae resort to blatantly visible warning (aposematic) coloration. Wasps and hornets, with their painful and dangerous stings, are commonly decorated with circular black bands alternating with yellow or white, and they are thereby recognized and respected by birds and animals. Many caterpillars employ a similar color pattern of alternating black and bright bands. Some are toxic and dangerous to eat by virtue of chemicals absorbed from the larval food plant; the monarch larva is a common example (fig. 13–4). Other larvae are presumably palatable and seem to be getting a "free ride" by using the warning coloration, as is the case with the larva of the black swallowtail (*Papilio polyxenes*, fig. 9–1).

Some moths imitate wasps quite directly. The clearwing moths (family Sesiidae) and the wasp moths (subfamily Ctenuchinae) have transparent, wasp-shaped wings, sometimes a narrowed "waist" between thorax and banded abdomen, elongated trailing hind legs, and a deliberately wasplike manner of hovering as they approach or feed at flowers. As you watch one closely, you gradually notice that the antennae are longer than those of a wasp and are quite mothlike; the hum of the wings is more subdued. But as with the bird-dropping imitators, it pays to be quite sure of your diagnosis!

HAIRS AND SPINES

Many caterpillars are covered with hairs or spines. Their significance to the caterpillar may be one thing, and to the caterpillar-watcher quite another. Humans may respond to them in various ways. Some are fascinated by their beauty and texture, others are fearful or repelled by their "ugliness." There can be wisdom in both reactions.

Very few larvae are completely naked. Many of those with apparently smooth skins nevertheless have a few fine hairs, so fine and sparse as to be scarcely noticeable. Their arrangement is not haphazard, as the hairs on our heads, but so orderly and regular that their locations can be used by experts for classification. About this, the less said the better. Caterpillar watchers have more interesting things to do than count hairs.

The hairs of interest are those that give a caterpillar its characteristic appearance. Tufts of hairs all the same length, black at both ends of the caterpillar and

Figure 12–8 Larva of a tussock moth (*Orgyia detrita*)

brown in the middle, serve to identify the woolly bear (*Pyrrharctia isabella*, fig. 2–1). The gray, yellow-spotted fellow with red head, two long brushes of black hair at the front end and one at the back, and four white tufts, like bits of toothbrush, on his back, is a tussock moth (*Orgyia detrita*, fig. 12–8). The milkweed plant with the herd of shaggy larvae decorated with raggedy black, brown, and white tufts is host to the harlequin caterpillar, larva of a rather dull, gray tiger moth (*Euchaetes egle*).

Eighteenth-century scientists seemed to believe that the fascinating colors and patterns of insects were created for mankind's pleasure. Since the insects and their larvae, with their colors and patterns, were enjoying this earth millions of years before humans were here to appreciate them, other uses are more likely. Since heavily haired caterpillars are not as palatable to birds as are smoother species, they have a definite protective advantage. The hairs adhere to and accumulate in the linings of birds' stomachs, causing irritation that makes most birds avoid them. The cuckoo, which eats great numbers of hairy tent caterpillars and gypsy moth larvae with obvious eagerness, has apparently developed the ability to shed the lining of its stomach and rid itself of the irritating hairs. No defense is perfect.

Most people can handle hairy caterpillars without concern, although some may develop specific contact allergies. One occasionally widespread problem, during gypsy moth outbreaks, is gypsy moth dermatitis, a very annoying, itchy rash. Shed caterpillars hairs, drifting in the air by the millions, are trapped under sweaty clothing, producing a skin eruption in susceptible people. Yet those same people may be able to handle the caterpillars with their fingers, which have tougher skin, without any problem. Caterpillar hairs on the fingers, however, if rubbed into the eyes, can cause irritation there. We are not aware of any similar problem occurring in birds, with regard to skin or eyes, so this is probably an accidental effect of the hairs, rather than one with a protective purpose.

Bristly and spiny plants are treated with a certain degree of respect by warm-blooded, soft-skinned animals, including lep-watchers. Should bristly and

Figure 12–9 Stinging larva of New England buck moth (*Hemileuca lucina*)

spiny caterpillars evoke the same emotions? The answer is an emphatic "yes!" —for a few species. The handsome, short, spiny, green-and-black slug caterpillar, aptly named saddleback in English, is not to be cuddled. Its Latin name, *Sabine stimulea*, weakly suggests caution. Its stinging spines can inflict an injury that can remain painful and swollen for days. One of our friends was hospitalized for a week after an encounter with a saddleback. Other slug caterpillars (limacodids) are similarly dangerous, as are the larvae of flannel moths (megalopygids).

Other larvae noted for their stinging spines are those of the buck moths (genus *Hemileuca*, fig. 12–9), and of the io moth (*Automeris io*) and its close relatives. The hollow, fluid-filled spines readily penetrate the skin and break off, giving the impression of a close encounter with some very vicious nettles. Yet some people with thick enough skin on their fingertips can handle these creatures with little discomfort. The eggs of

these hemileucine moths are laid in clusters (figs. 4–1, 5–1) and the larvae feed together, at least in the earlier instars.

But most spiny larvae can be handled perfectly safely. While mourning cloak larvae resemble those of buck moths, and also feed in groups, their spines are unarmed. Cecropia larvae, with their red-and-yellow, macelike knobs, are merely rough to the touch and do not sting. And the most fearsome-looking monster of them all, the hickory horndevil, larva of the royal walnut moth (*Citheronia regalis*), with long curved horns like a billy goat, covered with barbs, is sheer sham. The horns would be dangerous only to soap bubbles. We have read of no experiments to test whether birds, given equal opportunity, show any preference between smooth caterpillars and innocuous spiny ones, but it is reasonable to suspect that they, as we, think twice before reaching for them.

DISTRACTION _____

The habit of feeding in groups would seem to offer up the larvae as a banquet instead of a snack, but it has some definite advantages. Communal feeders such as the mourning cloak and the spiny oak worm (*Anisota stigma*) often twitch synchronously when disturbed. This sudden activation of a quiescent tangle of caterpillars can actually flick off egg-laying wasps or startle an inquisitive bird. When the oak worms are resting to-gether before moulting, they mimic a dead, skeletonized oak leaf (fig. 12–10). Yellow-necked apple worms (*Datana ministra*), when disturbed, curve both ends of the body sharply upward into a C shape, converting a peaceful group of feeding larvae into a many-pronged, hairy mass (fig. 12–11).

Butterflies roosting in groups are more difficult to see than single individuals. When zebra butterflies (*Heliconius char-*

Figure 12–10 Spiny oak worms (*Anisota stigma*), resting posture

Figure 12–11 Yellow-necked apple worms (*Datana ministra*), posturing

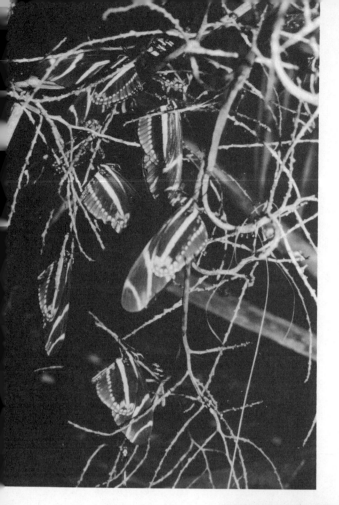

itonius) share a communal roost in a thicket, the resulting haphazard pattern of light and dark bands is impressive camouflage (fig. 12–12).

"Startle patterns" are a defense used by a number of larger moths. The io moth can suddenly bare its hind wings to reveal two large, blue-black eyespots. Several sphinx moths in the genera *Smerinthus* and *Paonias* have less elaborate but similarly suggestive hind wing spots. The drawn-out tip of the forewing of the huge Atlas moth (*Attacus atlas*) of eastern Asia has an eyespot giving the impression of a snake's head, full size (fig. 12–13). Any of these revelations should make a bird think twice!

The underwing moths use startle patterns in a less specific manner. Sudden uncovering of the hind wings flashes bands of red, orange, or yellow alternating with black, a variant of the "bright

Figure 12–12 Zebra butterflies (*Heliconius charitonius*) roosting in thicket

Figure 12–13 Atlas moth (*Attacus atlas*) showing "snake head" wing tips

plus black" banding worn by stinging insects (fig. 26–1). Researchers have shown that birds are alarmed by this.

Hairstreak butterflies resting on foliage practice an ingenious defense tactic. As the butterfly sits quietly, in plain view, it slowly moves its hind wings up and down, in an alternating motion, like a person rubbing both hands together. The lower corner of the hind wing usually bears a very fine "tail"—hence the name "hairstreak." The undersurface of that area of the wing is decorated with a red-and-black eyespot, and the wing corner is wrinkled outward a bit. This combination of tails, eyespot, and wrinkled corners creates the impression of a three-dimensional "false head" (fig. 17–1). The gentle motion of the hind wings directs the predator's attention to this area rather than to the butterfly's ac-

tual head, which is less conspicuous and is kept motionless. Many hairstreaks have the tails and eyespots missing from both hind wings, or have beak marks in that area, indicating that the strategy works, sacrificing expandable fragments of wing to protect vital areas of the body.

Many species of swallowtail butterflies also have eyespots and tails on the same area of the hind wings, and it is not unusual to find a specimen with these decorations symmetrically removed. This suggests that the false head is used by groups other than the hairstreaks. We also have a specimen of a geometrid moth from Ecuador with a pair of contrasting red and black eyespots on a corner of the upper surface of each hind wing. This area of one hind wing has been neatly removed by a lizard.

DIRECT ACTION

Moths and butterflies use their large compound eyes, which are larger in the day-flying species and smaller in those flying at night, to warn them of predators. Any suddenly perceived motion will make a flying insect dodge or dip, or startle a resting one into flight. The camera-carrying or net-wielding lep-watcher knows all about this!

Bats on the prowl emit supersonic squeaks, not just for echolocation of obstructions in their flight paths, but also to detect the flying moths that they hunt. Many groups of moths are able to hear and respond to these squeaks, and the noctuid moths have been studied in particular detail. A noctuid has, beneath each hind wing, a hollow pit equipped with an "eardrum" and two or three nerve cells attuned to the echolocation frequency emitted by the bat in flight. When the moth hears the warning, it quickly adopts an erratic, zigzag flight

pattern and heads for the safety of the ground, escaping the scooplike net formed by the attacking bat's wings.

Most of the foregoing has been concerned with protection from the point of view of human visual experiences. It is justifiable to assume that the viewpoint of birds and small mammals is rather similar. It is quite uncertain, however, whether these visual aspects of defense offer protection against insect and spider enemies. The nature of the visual image received by an insect's brain is scarcely known. They use a different portion of the spectrum of light, perceiving less in the longer wavelengths but utilizing the ultraviolet extensively. Their behaviour suggests that they pick up a great deal of information about their prey by chemical senses and by touch. The defenses lepidoptera have evolved against such approaches are only beginning to be studied.

Figure 13–1 Monarch (*Danaus plexippus*) and viceroy (*Limenitis archippus*)

Protection by Mimicry

Because of the complexity of this facet of lepidopterology, it seems appropriate to include a "program" to which the reader can refer.

Scent receptors in a butterfly's feet tell her where she must lay her eggs, and having laid them, her work is done. She flies away, mindless of what will result.

The caterpillars hatch. Their feet touch the leaf, stem, or blossom on which the eggs have been laid, and they begin to eat. When they are disturbed by any motion or sound, their instinct signals them to react, in order to avoid possible danger. Each species is pro-grammed, by virtue of having survived

CAST OF CHARACTERS (IN ORDER OF THEIR APPEARANCE)

Common Name	Latin Name	Family
Viceroy	*Limenitis archippus*	Nymphalidae
Monarch	*Danaus plexippus*	Danaidae
Pipe vine swallowtail	*Battus philenor*	Papilionidae
Queen	*Danaus gilippus*	Danaidae
Soldier	*Danaus eresimus*	Danaidae
Florida viceroy	*L. archippus floridensis*	Nymphalidae
Gold rim	*Battus polydamas*	Papilionidae
Spicebush swallowtail	*Papilio troilus*	Papilionidae
Black swallowtail	*Papilio polyxenes*	Papilionidae
Tiger swallowtail	*Papilio glaucus*	Papilionidae
Red spotted purple	*Limenitis astyanax*	Nymphalidae
Diana fritillary	*Speyeria diana*	Nymphalidae

over thousands of years, to become "invisible" or to appear unpalatable. Some strike weird postures and remain motionless, thus appearing to be a part of the plant that they have been eating. Others flaunt spiny filaments, protrude glands with noxious odors, or pose to resemble some undesirable creature.

Those with the most successful reactions are not eaten, and so become adults that lay eggs, and the cycle continues over thousands of years.

As colors, shapes, decorations, and reactions change, so do the caterpillars and chrysalids and butterflies and moths.

Survival depends upon how complete the camouflage is, and how adept the endangered creature is in its efforts to use its camouflage or any other defenses it may have.

Camouflage does undoubtedly save many lepidoptera from an untimely demise, but it is a passive approach at best, since it lacks any real involvement by either prey or predator. The life of the viceroy butterfly (*Limenitis archippus*) is an example of this laid-back approach to camouflage as a way of life.

From the beginning, the viceroy is a loner. The female lays one egg on the tip of a willow leaf—one lone egg for each chosen leaf. The egg is so small and translucent that it resembles a single drop of dew.

On hatching, the tiny caterpillar first eats its eggshell. It then begins to chop up the edges of the leaf, using its silk to wrap the bits into a ball. Still spinning silk, it suspends the ball from the leaf end, and there it remains for several days, looking very much like the egg mass of a small spider.

When this has been accomplished, the caterpillar, still no more than ¼" long, begins to build a shelter in which it can live in safety until the following spring.

It walks about on the leaf surface "measuring the cloth" before beginning the work of spinning and sewing. Next, starting at the tip of the leaf, it whittles away the outer edges for about ⅓" (more or less, depending on the species of willow), at the same time making a meal of the shavings. The result is an isosceles triangle about ⅓" long and about ¼" wide at the base. This small structure will eventually be the "roof" of its winter quarters.

Next it crawls about on the leaf, measuring the distance from end to end and from side to side. If the surface is too wide (as on a pussy willow), the caterpillar again cuts it to size. With each step of the operation, it takes measurements. When all the necessary cutting and shaving have been accomplished, it begins to construct a tube, starting at the base of the leaf and sewing the edges together. This whole process takes several days, but the result is a sturdy tube, waterproof and large enough to serve as winter quarters when it is time to hibernate.

Before this project is begun, the caterpillar has secured the leaf to the twig by binding it with silk, so that when autumn leaves begin to fall, the hibernaculum will remain securely attached until spring. As the leaf dries, the pointed tip curls down and functions as an awning or umbrella. The completed hibernaculum, now ready for occupancy, has taken the form of a Jack-in-the-pulpit, ¾" long. The "newborn" hides in it when not feeding and later hibernates in it until the following spring, when it awakens and creeps out of its nest to eat the succulent new leaves of the willow branch (fig. 13–2).

It grows and moults and is brown with a patch of white. Its camouflage makes it look like a bird dropping, and because it looks so inedible it is ignored by predatory birds. It grows and moults and looks more like a willow gall with each moult.

Figure 13–2 Two hibernacula and larvae of viceroy (*Limenitis archippus*)

In the fifth instar, it is brown, gray-white, and lumpy. Twiglike protrusions on its thorax and weird posturing make it seem part of the tree, a broken twig or crooked deformity (fig. 13–3). When it pupates, the chrysalis hangs like a dead and twisted leaf. It is able to assume such shapes even beyond the end of its larval life. When the butterfly emerges, its wings are bright orange bordered with black, the black dotted with white. There are white patches in the black tips of its forewings. Its wing veins are black, and the body is black mottled with white (fig. 13–1, right). It flies and it glides, and the message written on its orange-copper wings is: "Warning—poisonous!" But it is not poisonous. All its life it had been protected by its camouflage, protected so well that no bird had been

tempted to eat it. Now its whole life-style has changed. It is no longer camouflaged, it can no longer hide, and it is not poisonous. What is wrong?

In the meadows of Maine, the milkweed is two to three feet tall, silvergreen, and the monarch butterflies, as they pass through the meadows, deposit their eggs on the undersides of its leaves, one egg to a leaf.

When the eggs hatch, the newborns remain on the top side of their leaves. They begin to eat the silvery fuzz, and finally the edges of the new leaves; each little nibbled bit is edged with a thread of white latex.

Beginning with this small divergence of style, the life of the monarch is entirely different from the life of the viceroy. The monarch caterpillar has no camouflage, no posturing, no hiding place.

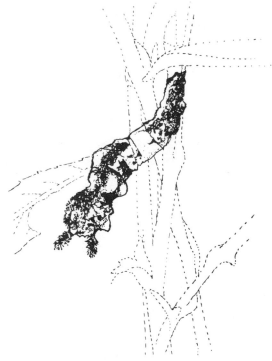

Figure 13–3 Last instar larva of viceroy (*Limenitis archippus*)

From the beginning, the caterpillar, small as it is, is glaringly colored. A predator small enough to be interested in this tiny splinter of life would see a striped and wrinkled body, alternately light and dark, black and creamy, feeding unafraid in broad daylight. It does not hide. It does not blend into anything but continues to feed with unconcern, shedding skin after skin, until its 2¼" length stretches diagonally across its chosen leaf (fig. 13–4). It eats until nothing but a fraction of the midrib remains. In broad sunlight it flaunts its chalky whiteness, wound with bands of glaring yellow and velvety black. The long, coal-black filaments on its thorax are in constant agitation. If it senses danger, it quickly rolls into a wheel and drops into the surrounding grass until danger has passed.

It may hang its chrysalis from the leaf

Figure 13–4 Last instar larva of monarch (*Danaus plexippus*)

of its food plant, but just as often it migrates to a twig, a board, the bottom edge of a shingle, the bottom edge of an outdoor chair. There it sheds its chalky skin and becomes a pendant of jade, too beautiful for human hands to destroy, too glaringly visible for foraging birds or animals to risk.

When the butterfly emerges, its wings are bright orange, bordered with black, the black dotted with white. There are white patches in the tips of its forewings. Its wing veins are black, and the body is black mottled with white (fig. 13–1, left). It flies and it glides, and the message written in black on its orange-copper wings is: "Warning: I am poisonous!"

The answer to this mystery of contrasting life cycles is that the adult viceroy is gaining protection against predators by mimicking the monarch. This is an effective ploy only because the monarch is poisonous to foraging birds.

Mimicry as a means of avoiding predation by birds is one of the most fascinating aspects of the study of butterflies. In the tropics where butterflies are abundant, the art of mimicry is so complex that it may never be thoroughly understood. It is much less prevalent in North America, but the fact that it does exist here as an instrument of survival is just as astonishing in a smaller way.

Butterfly mimicry exists primarily because birds eat caterpillars, probably hundreds of them every day. But do they know that not all caterpillars are edible? The answer is, "No, not until they have eaten the wrong one."

However, poisonous caterpillars do send out warning signals by means of their striking markings. The viceroy caterpillar, which is not poisonous, sends out no warning signals but depends on its camouflage in both larval and pupal stages to protect it from predators.

Therefore it must be the monarch caterpillars that the birds avoid. But how does a bird know that monarch caterpillars are poisonous?

Birds have to learn what to eat and not to eat by trial and error. A bird that eats a monarch caterpillar will become violently ill, vomit in about fifteen seconds, and not recover for about twenty minutes. After this experience it will not touch another monarch caterpillar. It will, in fact, teach its young not to eat such caterpillars by taking one in its beak, dangling it before the wide-open mouths of its fledglings, and then flinging it away into the underbrush, leaving them gaping.

No one knows what percentage of monarch caterpillars is saved by this bit of learning on the part of the birds, but the number of monarch butterflies that congregate in Mexico each year certainly indicates that, bird or no bird, the monarch is equipped to be master of its ancestral territory. Now the question is, how has the viceroy butterfly come to be a mimic of the monarch butterfly?

The monarch caterpillar is poisonous and inedible to birds because it eats milkweed. This milkweed contains substances called cardiac glycosides that are sequestered in the caterpillar and passed along to the butterfly. Thus the butterfly is protected from predation by the same poison. The unlucky bird that eats a monarch butterfly will have the same pangs as those suffered by the bird that ate a caterpillar of the monarch. This means that countrywide, during the great monarch migrations, caterpillars that hatch en route and butterflies in flight will be much less subject to predation by birds: song birds, kingbirds, jays, catbirds, an endless procession of hungry predators that cannot digest them and will never feed them to their offspring.

Monarch butterflies live less than a year at best. Although birds may live for ten years, it has been established that one encounter with a monarch is a never-to-be-forgotten experience.

The monarch, partly by virtue of its poisons, has been able to maintain huge populations.

The adult viceroy, probably over many millennia, has managed to become an almost perfect mimic of the monarch.

The birds, owing to the trauma of their first monarch experience, will not eat any butterfly looking at all like a monarch. Instead they eat butterflies looking least like a monarch, while those that look most like a monarch mate and thrive.

What did the original viceroy look like? How long did it take this "pseudomonarch" to become the nearly perfect image that it is today? Probably not hundreds of years, but hundreds of thousands of years. Today, the only feature that the viceroy retains of that far distant beginning is a black semicircular line across the middle of its hind wings, and this, too, may be slowly vanishing. Many viceroys have already been found on which this line is only partially or faintly formed, and a surprising number have been taken that have no such black lines at all across their hind wings!

This appears to be conclusive evidence that the viceroy has evolved and is still evolving as a mimic of the monarch butterfly.

The viceroy-monarch connection is perfectly clear-cut and forthright. But there is another case of mimicry among our butterflies that is not nearly so clearcut. In this case the model—the distasteful species—is the pipe vine swallowtail (*Battus philenor*), and it feeds on Dutchman's pipe (genus *Aristolochia*) in its larval stages.

This vine was recorded as poisonous

as long ago as 1798, in *A History of Plants Supposed to be Poisonous*, by Pierre Bulliard. How poisonous it is, and poisonous to what, is not yet wholly clear. I can remember that in my early youth, the beautiful blue-and-black butterflies were a part of the neighborhood fauna in the suburbs of Boston where we lived. I also remember that at that time a house was considered to be up-to-date if the veranda was adorned with one of these vines with their thick, rough stems and huge heart-shaped leaves that yearly pushed through an endless maze of snarled stems to face the sun. I also remember that a favorite pastime of little boys was to break off the flowers from the vine and walk around sucking the stems, pretending that they were smoking pipes.

All of this leads me to believe that Dutchman's pipe is not deadly, although it might well be distasteful to an uninformed bird. Indeed, if such were not the case, there would be no model and no mimic.

The male *philenor* is one of our most beautiful insects. Its forewings are velvet black, and its hind wings a dazzling iridescent blue, bordered with a crescent of pearly white spots. All four wings are minutely edged with white. The pattern is similar for both sexes, but the female is black and white only. The warning colors of both male and female occur on the underside of the hind wing, covering all but a small black oval: vivid iridescent blue, decorated with seven bright orange-red spots topped with white.

There is really no other butterfly in the United States that can be mistaken for the pipe vine swallowtail. The simplicity of the upper side of its wings is unique. The bold and threatening message imparted by its underwings sends an unmistakable warning to all potential enemies. The caterpillars, when fully grown, are black, covered with reddish fleshy tubercles. Eggs are laid in batches, and the caterpillars remain communal feeders for most of their larval lives. When disturbed, they run in several directions, waving their heads and long black filaments, and causing many birds to doubt the wisdom of adding such a questionable item to the family lunch.

There are only two members, besides the monarch, of the family Danaidae in the United States. The queen is one, a truly beautiful, monarch-size butterfly. Its wings are mahogany-colored, edged with black and tipped with miniature flakes of white; unlike the monarch, its wing veins are not outlined in black. It resides mainly in Florida and also eats poisonous milkweeds. Last there is the soldier, a seldom seen vagrant from the West Indies, which is also mahogany-colored. An interesting sidelight to the mimicry of the monarch is that, in southern Florida, where the mahogany-colored queen is prevalent, the Florida viceroy is also mahogany-colored. Once a mimic, always a mimic!

Beyond this little duo of nonconformity, the monarch has no other relatives in the United States.

On the other hand, the pipe vine swallowtail, *philenor*, belongs to a very large family, the Papilionidae. There are about thirty-five members of the family, counting various forms, subspecies, and regional differences. At least thirty of these belong to the genus *Papilio*. Only two belong to the genus *Battus*.

The gold rim, *Battus polydamus*, is a rather rare butterfly in the United States. It is also the only swallowtail in the United States that does not have tailed wings. It occurs mainly on the Florida coast and in Texas, but not in sufficient numbers in either location to have induced mimicry.

Philenor resides in many parts of the country. It occurs in varying numbers from southern New England south to Florida, west to Arizona, and north to the Great Lakes. It is also found in lesser numbers in Nebraska and Colorado; there is a subspecies on the West Coast. The caterpillars of both *polydamus* and *philenor* feed on *Aristolochia* and are therefore distasteful to birds.

There is one feature by which these two poisonous butterflies can be distinguished from all of the nonpoisonous swallowtails. All other North American swallowtails have red eyespots on the inner angles of their hind wings. *Philenor* and *polydamus* do not.

The largest populations of *philenor* occur in the Appalachian region—especially Georgia, Kentucky, and Virginia—an area where many familiar butterflies occur, including the spicebush swallowtail (*P. troilus*) and the black swallowtail (*P. polyxenes*). Females of both species are considered to be mimics of *philenor*. The females of both species have black forewings and large areas of iridescent blue on the hind wings. On the undersurface of the hind wings, there are two rows of red spots, as opposed to *philenor*'s one.

Of the thirty or more remaining North American swallowtails, there are seven that look enough like *philenor* to be mimics, but they all exist in the Far West (Arizona, Montana, California) where *philenor* is scarce. A mimicry complex cannot be established unless there are more poisonous models than there are potential mimics.

It all seems somewhat incredible, except for one other butterfly that erases all possible doubt that *philenor* is mim-

icked. This is the tiger swallowtail (*P. glaucus*), the large bright-yellow-and-black butterfly that is found in every state east of the great plains and is the ultimate goal of every child who ever wielded a butterfly net.

In the Appalachian region, the butterfly has a dark form that is a more convincing disguise than that of either of the "full-time" mimics (*troilus* and *polyxenes*). On the dorsal side, its forewings are velvety black. This variation alone is astonishing. How many years—centuries—would be needed for a brilliantly yellow butterfly to become black? Its hind wings are black, overlaid with iridescent blue; on the underside, the red spots are in a single row as on the underwings of *philenor*. It is, in fact, an almost perfect mimic.

Strangely enough (or perhaps not so strangely) two other butterflies are thought to be mimics of *philenor*. Both belong to the family Nymphalidae. One is the red spotted purple (*Limenitis arthemis astyanax*) and the other is the Diana fritillary (*Speyeria diana*). Both occur in Appalachia. Both are bright iridescent blue and black, with fine white borders. Being nymphalids, they do not have tailed wings. *Astyanax* has some red decorations on the undersides of its wings and is more or less the shape of a *Papilio*. *Diana* has no such qualifications. It is a "square" butterfly if ever there was one, and uncommonly large. Calling it a mimic of *philenor* may seem like a wild guess, but seeing both male and female together gives one pause. The wings of the male Diana fritillary are a plain deep brown with a ½" border of orange, the colors of almost all other fritillaries.

A female does not change her colors without reason!

CHAPTER

14

On the Uses of Silk

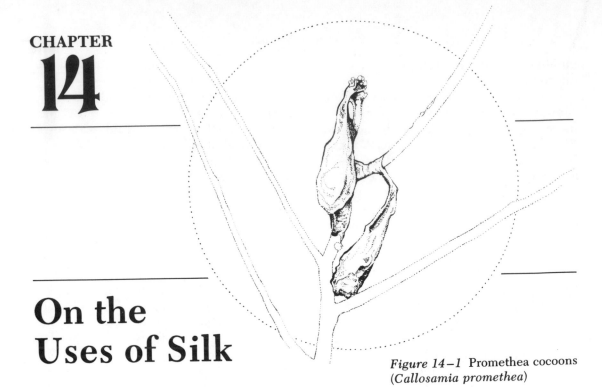

Figure 14–1 Promethea cocoons (*Callosamia promethea*)

Silk and caterpillars are an inseparable combination, because without silk and the ability to use it, no caterpillar could survive. Silk enters into every aspect of its life. To sit and watch a caterpillar as it patiently spins is to know once and for all that a caterpillar is not a worm. It is fully equipped and prepared to meet all the necessary steps to adulthood, beginning on the day it chews its way out of an eggshell, and ending when it casts off its last larval skin and becomes a chrysalis or pupa.

All larvae are prepared to produce silk as soon as they hatch from their eggs. The silk is extruded from a modified salivary gland, called a spinneret, located just below the caterpillar's chewing mandibles. With the aid of a magnifying glass, one can see a newly hatched larva waving its head from side to side as

it lays down a nearly invisible strand. It spins as it walks, and as it walks, it clutches the minute silken carpet it has made with equally minute hooks at the ends of its prolegs. Because of this device, it is safe from the hazard of falling to the ground in wind or in rain or at any time, since leaves are usually slippery.

The silk spun by a caterpillar also acts as anchor for a lifeline, should the caterpillar for some reason be dislodged. If confronted by a potential predator, it can disengage all its hooked feet and drop from its leaf while still spinning. Having escaped from predation, the caterpillar may remain dangling from its silken lifeline until a breeze blows it against a new foothold; it may continue its descent, or it may return to its original perch, consuming its spun silk en route.

Without the ensurance provided by

this lifesaving device, many fallen caterpillars would land so far from their food sources that they would be unable to make their way back.

The spinneret is the one essential tool awarded at birth to all caterpillars. It has multiple uses that affect almost every aspect of their lives. This valuable asset is used in different ways by many different kinds of caterpillars. The well-known but little-liked gypsy moth (*Lymantria dispar*) is one example. The female lays all her eggs on one tree and cements them together in a mass covered with a thatch of hairs from her abdomen. The following spring, the caterpillars all hatch at the same time and immediately begin to disperse, with a strategy known as "ballooning." They spin silk out into the air, tiny wisps of silk lofted by the slightest breeze. When the strands are long enough to lift their weight, the caterpillars loosen their grip on the tree and sail away to some other tree. Small wonder that they are called "gypsy" moths!

The life of an American tent caterpillar is entirely different. The female moth (*Malocosoma americanum*) lays her eggs on a twig (usually cherry, apple, or some other related fruit tree). When the caterpillars hatch the following spring, they move to a crotch in a branch and build a communal tent of silk. There they will live, making several forays during day and night to feed on nearby leaves. The larger they grow, the larger the nest they make. When full grown, they leave the tree and disperse, each finding its own place to pupate. They spin powdery cocoons by injecting a chemical substance among the strands as they are spun. Two weeks later, the moths emerge.

Silk is also used as an anchor for the caterpillar preparing to shed its skin, since its old skin has become so tight

that it cannot slip out "gracefully." It spins a small mound of silk on a leaf of its food plant. It then walks carefully over this small silk "button" until the last pair of prolegs reaches it and is solidly hooked into it. The caterpillar can then force itself forward within its old skin until the skin splits at the thorax. Now it can easily crawl out of its anchored skin and begin its next instar.

Some measuring worms (geometrid larvae) have an interesting trick. At rest, they grasp a small branch with their last two pairs of prolegs, holding their bodies out at an angle to give the appearance of dead twigs. A silken thread, spun from the caterpillar's head to the branch, acts as a guyline to maintain the body at a constant angle.

Spinning silk is always a survival technique, whether employed by moth or butterfly larvae. The ubiquitous vanessid butterflies (the painted lady, Hunter's butterfly, and the red admiral) are experts at tent building during their larval stages. Each caterpillar builds its own nest. The caterpillar of the painted lady makes its nest on thistle, Hunter's butterfly on species of cudweed and pearly everlasting, and the red admiral on stinging nettle. Building the shelter is almost concurrent with eating, but the product serves as a blind against predators, even in the early stages. The nests on thistle can be quite handsome when first finished. The caterpillar of the painted lady incorporates the spines of the thistle into the nest, perhaps as a deterrent to uninvited guests. The Hunter's caterpillar decorates its nest with petals of pearly everlasting, but the nest of the red admiral is far from artistic. The larva pulls and sews together a rather disordered cave of adjacent leaves, and then proceeds to sleep, eat, and deposit its excrement therein. The walls, floor, and ceiling are consumed. The spun silk has a snarled appearance, and the shelter's spiny black inhabitants add nothing of aesthetic merit to the nettle patch. The skeletonized den fills up with frass (droppings), and the caterpillar moults and moves elsewhere on the plant to form a new one.

In contrast to these rather disordered shelters made by nymphalid larvae are the neat and tidy shelters made by larvae of some of the dusky wing skippers (genus *Erynnis*). They also sew together adjacent leaves, but they move out of the house into nearby foliage to do their eating; they sleep at home, and if they wish to dispose of excrement, they turn their backs to the door and fire the pellets of frass a distance of several feet! The result is a clean abode that can be used for an extended period.

The first instar larva of the red spotted purple (*Limenitis astyanax*) has a peculiar habit. It sews little pellets of frass

and chewed vegetation into a narrow "gangplank" that juts out from the edge of the leaf it is eating (fig. 14–2). When it rests its rough brown form on the plank between meals, it passes easily for a shred of withered vegetation.

The spicebush swallowtails (*Papilio triolus*) and tiger swallowtails (*Papilio glaucus*) begin life by spinning tiny walkways on the tips of the leaves of their food plants. These pads are spun tightly and act not only as little trampolines on which the caterpillars rest, but as hideouts, because the tautly spun strands draw the edges of the leaves together, forming a tube. A new and larger tube is constructed after each moult. By the time the caterpillars are in the fourth instar, they are decorated with eyelike spots on the thorax, which cause them to resemble the heads of small snakes. By the fifth instar, both species are bright green, and the eye spots are even more threatening. Many a nature lover, sud-

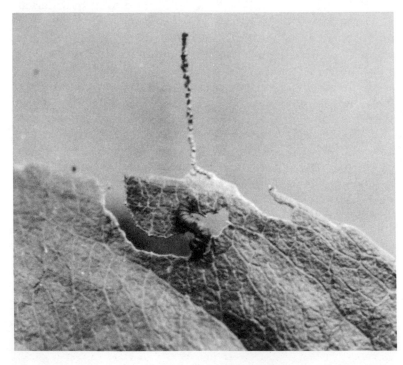

Figure 14–2 "Gangplank" of first instar of red spotted purple larva (*Limenitis astyanax*)

denly discovering one of these on a leafy branch of sassafras or cherry, would think twice before trying to discover what the length of its body might be! Many a butterfly has owed its wings to the few strands of silk so painstakingly woven together to make this shelter.

The larvae of swallowtails, sulphur butterflies, and whites have evolved another use for silk that makes the emergence of the butterfly an easier process than the somersaulting headfirst dive of the Nymphalidae. This is a "seatbelt" that the caterpillar spins across its back after securing its anal prolegs in a silk button. The nymphalids and the danaids (monarchs), when ready to pupate, merely spin the silk button, fasten their anal prolegs into it, release their other prolegs, and dangle upside down to shed the last larval skin.

The papilios, sulphurs, and whites are held against the surface of their choice by their seatbelts; when they emerge as butterflies, they can crawl forth and expand their wings in place gracefully, without any gymnastics.

Many moths that spend their larval lives in trees leave the tree to pupate. Among these is a tiny caterpillar named *Bucculatrix ainsliella*. It is almost too small to be seen as it mines between the surfaces of leaves, but during a year when the species is free from disease, predators, and parasites, they appear by the thousands. During the night, they leave the oak trees, where they have been feeding, by spinning lifelines as much as forty feet long, which carry them to or near to the ground. They pupate almost at once. Their cocoons are white and look like grooved grains of rice. They seem to appear out of nowhere on window sills, picnic tables, under porch rails, behind blinds, even in crevices of automobiles left outdoors overnight. They make their descent en masse, and as they descend, their silk covers smaller trees from top to bottom, as though with a translucent veil, a truly lovely sight in the early morning sunlight.

Most persistent of the structures made from silk are the cocoons of moths, particularly those made by the large silkmoths (fig. 14–1). So durable are they that they may be found attached to trees years after their architects have emerged and flown off. It was the durability of these strands of silk that enabled the oriental silkworm to reach the pinnacle of importance it has held for the past four or five millennia.

BOMBYX MORI

This section could be titled "The Most Important Caterpillar in the World," or perhaps "Never Underestimate the Power of a Caterpillar." There are many legends as to how long ago it all began. Some say five thousand years ago. One legend tells us that the discovery was made by a young girl named Luoa Tzu, more than three thousand years ago. Another, called the Hsi Ling-Shih Legend, says that it was first discovered in the garden of the Emperor Huang Ti, called the Yellow Emperor.

All the legends seem to agree that the discovery was made by a young woman who, walking in a garden, saw a small egg-shaped object on a twig of mulberry. She broke off the twig, took it home, and noticed that it was made of hair-thin threads that could not be unwound. When she shook it, it rattled. She immersed the "egg" in warm water. This dissolved a sticky substance, and she was then able to unwind the strand, which gradually became tighter and stiffer and hard to unwind. Again she dampened it in warm water and more of the sticky substance dissolved.

When all the thread had been painstakingly unwound, what she found was a small smooth object, oval in shape, and the color of sandalwood, and it glistened as though polished. It was a treasure, an enigma to be contemplated every day.

On the tenth day, she returned to admire it for the tenth time and found it torn and crumpled. But beside it there was a small pale moth. Its wings were as white and iridescent as pearls, smooth, and exquisitely curved. Its body was large and densely covered with white hair, softer and shorter than the hair on a newborn child.

This, so goes the legend, was the day the silk industry was born.

Legends are often far removed from fact, and there is little chance that anyone will ever be able to prove exactly when and where in China a little moth was discovered to be capable of producing a wisp of silk that would eventually be woven into the most beautiful and the most expensive fabrics in the world.

The Chinese were able to guard the secret of silkmaking from the rest of the world for more than two thousand years, but eventually, so the story goes, a monk, or a person disguised as a monk, managed to smuggle out a few cocoons by hiding them in a hollow bamboo staff. The silk industry soon blossomed in Europe, as thousands of little caterpillars spun their lives away, and the royalty of Europe became clad in silks and satins and flowery brocades.

It is safe to say that no craftsman, artist, or purveyor to the ruling class has ever contributed more to the prestige or the self-image of its members than did the little silkworms whose cocoons were so laboriously spun, only to be dismantled by human hands before the larvae within them had become pupae or changed into moths.

No one knows what this original silk moth was really like, because it has been domesticated for so long. Today the bodies of the females are nearly twice as long as those of other moths with similar wing spans. The female can no longer fly but is confined to a small cage, where after mating she lays from three hundred to five hundred eggs. These are kept in cold storage to overwinter until, brought out of hibernation the following spring, they hatch in twenty days, in spotlessly clean surroundings, attended by workers masked to prevent disease.

The young caterpillars are given fresh mulberry leaves every two or three hours, day and night. They moult four times. At this point they are up to seventy times their original size and are 3″ long.

When making their cocoons, the caterpillars spin for three days, sending out the fine liquid stream that dries and becomes silk. When finished, the cocoons may be brown, or they may be translucent green or a pale peach color, and inside each one the caterpillar that made it is preparing to pupate. Some are allowed to do so and later emerge to mate and begin the cycle anew, but most never see the light of day again. The cocoons must be boiled or soaked in hot water in order to dissolve the sticky substance used by the caterpillar to cement the silk into the cocoon. When the silk has been removed and spooled, the workers sometimes crack open the pupal shells with their teeth and eat the cooked pupa—a nutritious delicacy.

The silk is spun, dyed, and woven into the most exquisite fabrics the world has ever known: ceremonial garments for both men and women, multicolored brocades, upholstery for chairs, embroidery, the thinnest of veils, and the softest of carpets. The work begun by innumerable little caterpillars can be seen and admired in the most prestigious museums of the world.

PART III

On the Matter of Names

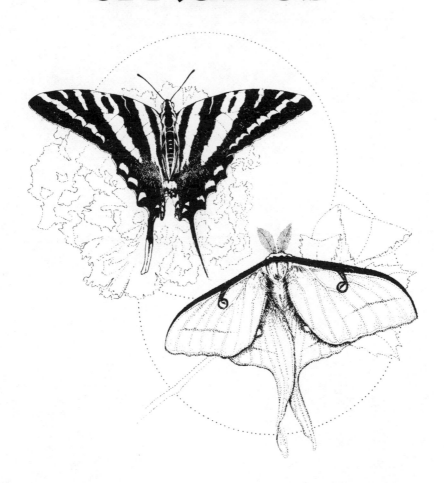

CHAPTER 15

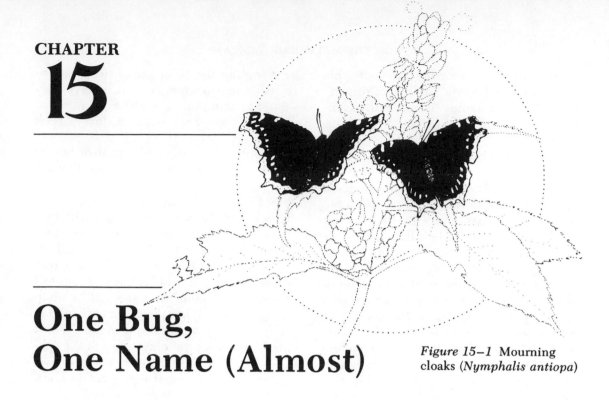

One Bug, One Name (Almost)

Figure 15–1 Mourning cloaks (*Nymphalis antiopa*)

When people wish to talk with one another about different kinds of butterflies, it is a great convenience that the butterflies have names. You could discuss "the large orange butterfly with black wing veins and wing margins that frequents milkweed blossoms," but would you be talking about the monarch or the viceroy? When you say that you are talking about the monarch, any uncertainty is resolved. A monarch is a monarch, and a viceroy is a viceroy. Fine.

But common names are not entirely reliable. If butterfly watchers from southern California and Pennsylvania converse about the "gray hairstreak," they are not talking about the same bug. The westerner's gray hairstreak is *Satyrium tetra*; the easterner's is *Strymon melinus*. "Oh, you mean the common

hairstreak," says the westerner, and draws a blank stare. The East does not have a "common hairstreak." Again, someone who learned a butterfly's name many years ago may not use the same language as a more recent student. The oldster may speak of the "thistle butterfly" and "Hunter's butterfly." The names "painted lady" and "American painted lady" are now in more common use. Who is to say which names are more satisfactory? Talk with an Englishman and the confusion mounts. Your "mourning cloak" is his "Camberwell beauty." Your "ringlets" are his "heaths." His "ringlet" is in a genus that does not occur in North America, but when he travels to other parts of Europe the "ringlets" he recognizes there are your "alpines." But your traveling friend's troubles have only begun. In the countries he visits, his "Camberwell beauty" and his "ringlet" have different names in each native language, and the uncertainty is compounded.

So it is with butterflies. What is the situation with moths? Many of the larger or more colorful moths have common names that are in reasonably widespread use, but a great many of the smaller moths have none, unless they are pretty or have the distinction of being important agricultural pests. Considering the fact that there are about 10,500 species of moths in the United States and Canada (as compared with about 750 species of butterflies), it is not surprising that a majority of the moths have no common names. Publishers of two recently issued field guides attempted to remedy this problem—if it is a problem—by requiring their authors to produce common names for all species. In the case of the butterflies, the task was accomplished, but not without anguish. The author of the moth guide tried valiantly to comply, in many instances adapting traditional British terminology with creditable success. Fortunately his publisher relaxed the requirement when it came to the micro-moths, and many of them were allowed to remain without common names.

The traditional British names have the attraction of being quaint, with their prominents, sallows, angles, carpets, waves, angle shades, pinions, brocades, wainscots, owlets, quakers, arches, darts, and daggers. Unfortunately, sometimes variations on these names are applied to species that are not closely related, although they may have been thought to be related when they were first used in the eighteenth century. Whether such names will ever catch on in the Western Hemisphere is uncertain.

Adopting the language of the lepidopterist is not for everyone. It involves becoming acquainted with a number of Latin words and even a few Greek words.

People who have had a year or two of basic Latin can probably handle the scientific terminology without much trouble. People who have been interested in Greek and Roman mythology will also have a head start, since a great many butterflies and moths have been named for Greek and Roman heroes. Digging into these aspects of lepidopteran study will seem superfluous to some and a challenge to others, but the point of this book is to enjoy butterflies and moths. If you are happy with the nicknames of the species mentioned in this book, no one is going to fault you. If you want to learn the lepidopterous lingo, read on!

The great Swedish natural scientist of the eighteenth century, Carolus Linnaeus (1707–1778), was the first to bring order out of chaos, with his *Systema Naturae* (1758). He employed a system of names, arranged somewhat like a genealogy, for all the known insects, animals, and plants. The names were all composed of Latin (and some Greek) words, Latin being the written language of science in those days. He even tried to group the names, so that names that were associated with classical mythology were used for butterflies that he thought were related.

According to his system, the animal kingdom, all animal life, was sorted into major divisions, or *phyla*. Butterflies and moths, being animals, were included in the phylum Arthropoda (from *arthron*, meaning "joint," and *podos*, meaning "foot"). Next, the phylum was divided into *classes*, of which the class Insecta (from a Latin word meaning "cut in," referring to the constricted areas of an insect's body) might be called the first branch of the butterfly's family tree.

After this, Linnaeus separated "Insects Having Complete Metamorphosis" (insects whose development went from egg to larva to chrysalis to winged insect). This group was divided into various *orders*, including the order Lepidoptera.

The word lepidoptera is derived from two Greek words, *lepis*, meaning "scale," and *pteron*, meaning "wing." Lepidoptera are the scale-winged insects, because the wing membranes are covered with minute scales, which can be seen clearly only with a microscope or a strong hand glass.

The Lepidoptera were then divided into two suborders, the Rhopalocera, or butterflies, and the Heterocera, or moths. Rhopalocera is a Greek word meaning "club-ended." It refers to the antennae of the butterflies, which terminate in a small club. Heterocara is also a Greek word, meaning "other-ended." Moths have antennae of several sorts, but none of them ends with a club.

This is only the beginning. There is next a *family*, then a *genus*, and finally, the *species*. Each moth or butterfly is known by a pair of names. The first, the genus, serves to identify various organisms as being related to one another. The second, the species, is unique for each type of organism. The attention of the beginning lep-lover needs to start no earlier than separating butterflies from moths, and learning the differences among families. Then, as you become acquainted with various moths and butterflies, the genera and species fall into place.

The system has held up well, but it has had its problems. As knowledge of the relationships among different organisms has increased, many of the associations assumed by Linnaeus have turned out to be incorrect. New genera have had to be named, and some species have been moved into the new genera. Workers in different parts of a continent, unknown to each other, independently described the same species, or genus, using different names. When the species or genera later were recognized as identical, one name had to be discarded. In other instances, a single species turned out in fact to be two or more species, not readily distinguished when first studied. Many times the distinctions are mainly in the larval stage, or in characteristics of behavior or flight period. Yet rearing experiments can also have the opposite effect: two types of moths having sharply different markings, and different names, may regularly be reared as offspring from the same parent. They are therefore the same species, and the name of one must be discarded.

An example of this confusion is a common cutworm moth, the black-letter dart, to which Linnaeus gave the name *Noctua c-nigrum*. For over two centuries, it went by that name, until researchers determined that it should more properly be placed in the genus *Xestia*, and that in North America the species was (were!) two separate species, *dolosa* and *adela*, each distinct from the European *c-nigrum*. So now there are the greater black-letter dart (*dolosa*), the black-letter dart (*c-nigrum*), and the lesser black-letter dart (*adela*). The larvae of all three species are called the spotted cutworm!

If all this seems overwhelming, don't despair! We do need names in order to communicate, and the Latin binomial system of Linnaeus serves us well, both over time and throughout the world. Changing of a name, after all, is nothing unusual. It happens to nearly half our friends in the course of time, and they remain the same fine people. Furthermore, the changes are not capricious. They are made according to the rules of the International Code of Zoological Nomenclature, whose guardians carry out their deliberations with the caution of a snail executing a 180° turn.

You may shy away from the use of Latin names for fear that your pronunciation may not be correct. This may intimidate you in the presence of professional lepidopterists. Forget it! Listen to six lepidopterists and you will hear four different sorts of pronunciation, which causes them no concern. They understand one another, and they will understand you even if you botch a few. It's what you have to say that matters, not where your accents fall. As mentioned before, lepidopterists are a congenial lot.

Latin names are here to stay, and for many of the bugs we watch there are no others available. We might as well begin to like them.

16

The Families

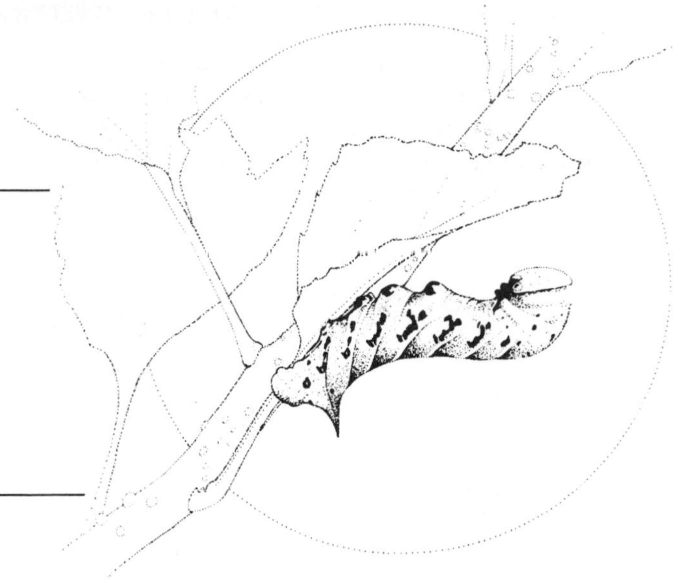

Figure 16–1 Small-eyed sphinx larva (*Paonias myops*)

Families within the order Lepidoptera are rather broad groups whose members share particular physical features and behavioral characteristics. Familiarity with the more prominent families makes it easier to recognize and identify new acquaintances.

The groups described briefly here are all dealt with as though they were families, although in some of the field guides and references some of the groups are called subfamilies. This detail is of little practical significance to the lep-watcher, whose interest is in learning to place a particular species in its proper group,

based on appearance and behavior.

The sequence presented here does not always follow the systematic order used by entomologists. A few butterfly families, dozens of small families of moths, and families of very small moths are omitted, despite the fact that they may be very common, beautiful in their own small-scale fashion, or fascinating in their life histories. Zoological family names are conventionally written with the suffix *-idae*. In this book we have usually used the Anglicized form ending in *-id* or *-ids*.

BUTTERFLIES

Papilionids—*swallowtail butterflies*. Usually large, "tails" on hind wings, often extrusible scent organs (osmateria) on the front of the caterpillar's thorax, chrysa-

lis suspended with a silk girdle. Includes the primitive parnassians, of cool climates, which have no tails and make no pupal girdle.

Pierids—*"whites" and sulphur butterflies*. Medium-size, some with scales that reflect ultraviolet light, caterpillars usually green and inapparent, chrysalis suspended with a silk girdle.

Lycaenids—*coppers, hairstreaks, and blues*. Small and sometimes very colorful butterflies, larvae sluglike, often eating buds or blossoms, some species tended by ants, pupa often concealed among leaf litter.

Riodinids—*metalmarks*. Small, frequently drab butterflies, often with metallic spots on both surfaces of the wings. Many more species in tropics, often brilliantly colored.

Nymphalids—*"brushfooted" butterflies*. The first pair of legs is reduced to small brushlike structures with some sensory functions; only the second and third pairs of legs are used for walking; very large size range; caterpillars often spin shelters, some species feed in groups; chrysalis always supended from silk button, with no girdle.

Heliconians. Colorful, long-winged, medium-size, subtropical and tropical; the butterflies can digest pollen and live many months; larvae feed on passion vine; adults are toxic to predators.

Satyrids—*wood nymphs and satyrs*. Brown, medium-size, metallic eyespots on wings; larvae feed mainly on grass; pendant chrysalis.

Danaids—*monarch, queen*. Large, robust, orange or brown; larvae concentrate cardiac glycosides from milkweed, making larva and adult toxic to predators; pendant chrysalis adorned with metallic spots.

Hesperiids—*skippers*. Antennae have point or hook on the knob; heavy-bodied, small or medium-size, fast fliers; larvae on grasses, bean family, various other plants; usually pupate in loosely sewn leaf shelter.

Megathymids—*giant skippers*. Antennae have plain knobs like other butterflies; heavy-bodied, medium-size to large, very fast fliers; larvae bore in yucca and agave, pupate in larval tunnel.

MOTHS

Saturniids—*silk moths, royal and imperial moths, buck moths*. Medium-size to very large; feathered antennae, do not feed as adults; broad wings, some with transparent windows; larvae often spiny, some stinging; some make cocoons.

Sphingids—*sphinx moths, hawkmoths*. Medium-size to very large; heavy, mostly plain antennae, cigarlike bodies, narrow wings, fast flight, hover while feeding; larva usually has horn at back end, hence

name "hornworm"; pupate on or under ground.

Arctiids—*tiger, wasp, and lichen moths*. Small to medium-size, often black with contrasting red markings; male antennae comblike, female hairlike; heavy bodies; larvae very hairy, eat many low plants, including lichens, often hibernate half-grown; pupa in thin cocoon incorporating caterpillar hairs.

Noctuids—*cutworm moths, underwings, deltoids*. Antennae hairlike or comblike; very small to very large, usually heavy-bodied, robust, fast fliers, usually drab gray or brown, occasionally brilliantly banded hind wings; larvae and food plants very varied; pupa usually on the ground.

Geometrids—*inchworm moths*. Small to medium, light-bodied, broad-winged (proportions of a butterfly), fluttering flight, some females wingless; male antennae usually comblike; larvae are loopers, eat many sorts of plants; pupa usually on the ground.

Notodonts—*prominents*. Heavy-bodied medium-size moths, dully colored; larvae bizarre in shape and color; pupa in hard cocoon, or on or in ground.

Lasiocampids—*lappet moths, tent caterpillar*. Medium heavy-bodied gray or brown moths, male and female antennae comblike; hairy larvae sometimes make communal webs; pupate in cocoon.

Lymantriids—*tussock moths*. Medium-size, heavy-bodied, drab, some females wingless, or winged but flightless; comblike antennae, diminutive or absent tongue; hairy larvae with tufts, usually tree feeders; loose cocoon.

Sesiids—*clearwing moths*. Wings often transparent, look more like wasps than moths; larvae bore in trees and soft plants.

Cossids—*carpenterworm moths*. Mouth parts nonfunctional; female much larger than male; males mistaken for sphinxes but have a hard and shiny look; larvae spend several years boring in trees.

Hepialids—*ghost moths*. Primitive, medium-size to quite large moths, swarm at dusk; larvae bore in roots.

Pyralids. One of the largest families, medium-size to small moths, hairlike antennae, rather delicate bodies and legs; larvae of many varied habits.

Tortricids. Another very large family of mostly small moths; forewings seem rectangular at the ends; larvae tie or roll leaves, or bore in fruits, stems, and roots.

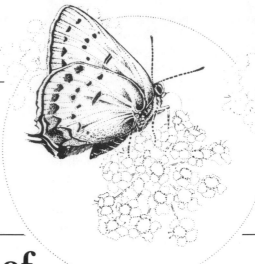

Identification of Moths and Butterflies

Figure 17–1 Acadian hairstreak (*Satyrium acadica*)

From past encounters you may have become familiar with the names of a few moths and butterflies, and you will pick up the names of many more from colleagues who may have been watching a bit longer. But most of the new moths and butterflies that come to your attention will have to be identified from books, or from comparison with specimens in collections of friends and in local museums.

Excellent books of several types are available. One of the most useful is the field guide, which illustrates each species quite clearly, points out the most significant identifying details, and gives concise information as to range, habitat, flight period, broods, and larval food plants, to the extent that these details are known. As the name implies, these books are small enough to fit into a pocket or pack and are easy to carry along on an outing. As mentioned in chapter 3, however, accurate field identification may be difficult or impossible, even when the insect is feeding quietly only a few inches away. Field guide coverage is now available for the butterflies of all of North America north of Mexico, but the single guide available for moths covers only that portion of North America east of the 100th meridian.

The larger reference books are invaluable, but, of course, more expensive. Some, while old and out of print, are widely available in public libraries and are still extremely useful for their extensive illustrations. Newer books, also extensively illustrated, have the added advantage of more detailed information on food plants and on adult behavior. These books, while up-to-date, are not the last word. As you work in the field, you will record equally valid and valuable information, which could very well find its way into a later edition. In these references, the moths, again, have less than ideal coverage. Books that cover all parts of the country and all the families of moths cannot possibly include all ten thousand species. The books that include all the species in a particular family of moths have, thus far, been completed for only a small number of families.

Another type of publication is regional in nature, covering a geological region, a state, or even smaller areas of particular interest to the author. Some are well illustrated, and some refer to illustrations in larger reference works. Text may range from extensive descriptions of each insect and its occurrence and behavior, down to simple listing of species and flight periods, with distribution by counties. Availability of these publications is often somewhat limited; public and university libraries are useful places to look.

Specific books that are most widely useful and available are listed and described briefly in our bibliography beginning on page 183.

Using these books for identification is primarily a matter of comparison. You try to match your recollection, your field description, your photograph, or the specimen in hand with the photograph or painting in the book. You then verify that the stated range, flight period, and habitat coincide reasonably with your observations. Don't forget to consider the size. Do the undersurfaces of the wings match up, as well as the uppers? And are you sure that you are dealing with a butterfly, and not a moth—are you using the right book? The printed information is seldom complete; range extensions and off-season flights are often seen. But if that moth you caught in Vermont looks just like a species listed only for New Mexico, or your skipper photographed in May seems to be a dead ringer for a species that flies only at the end of August, reopen the books and do a little more research.

Identifying caterpillars is another matter. Most of the books have illustrations of a few larvae, usually one or two species from each of the major families. If your caterpillar is one of those species, the job is easy. If you have at least a suspicion as to the family to which the larva belongs, comparison with text descriptions and food plant preferences may give the necessary clues. More often, however, the approach is longitudinal. Some larvae are identifiable because you have reared them from eggs from a female you identified. Others will be identifiable only when you have reared the caterpillar to maturity and discovered what moth or butterfly it produces. This, for us, is one of the best parts of lepwatching: observing the entire life cycle from beginning to end.

As you look through the books on butterflies, particularly of the western part of the country, you will notice that a lot of them have three Latin names, rather than two. The third name is for the *subspecies*. What is a subspecies?

If a population of a butterfly or moth has been on an island for a long time, out of touch with the mainland, changes in pattern and form can gradually occur. This changed population is called a subspecies. It could still mate successfully with the original population, if given a chance.

If the "island" is a mainland area that has become physically isolated over time by the intrusion of a mountain range or an intervening arid area, a subspecies can develop there. This has happened in many places in western North America, where hundreds of subspecies have been described. In the East, where there are few such barriers, subspecies are recognized mainly in a few isolated bogs or on mountaintops.

A subspecies should be identified by where you found it, not by what it looks like! It may vary considerably in a particular area, so that a variant of a checkerspot in Alberta, for example, can look just like the typical Utah subspecies. If this seems to be too much to accept, just stick with the species, and you will not go wrong.

This subspecies dilemma is also illustrated by the viceroy on the East Coast. In the North, the viceroy is a bright tawny orange color. The subspecies of viceroy found in Florida is a rich mahogany brown. You will occasionally see a mahogany-colored viceroy in the North, reared from eggs from a parent of normal northern color, and having siblings also of normal color. Such an individual is not of the subspecies *floridensis*, but merely a variant that looks like it. A subspecies is a whole local population, not just an individual.

PART **IV**

To Collect or Not to Collect?

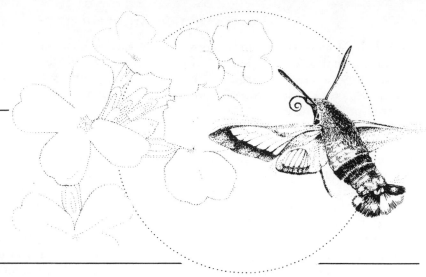

An Individual Decision

Figure 18–1 Hummingbird clearwing (*Hemaris thysbe*)

Until the last decade or so, the majority of people who were willing to admit an interest in moths and butterflies (and such an interest was definitely looked down upon by more macho types) made collecting these insects their primary activity. They caught, killed, prepared, and saved specimens. For some the goal was a collection of "Oh! My!" beauties. For others, the interest was in the species of a particular area or in concentration on a special family or group. Still others were armchair collectors, purchasing specimens from all parts of the world. Such collecting still has many adherents, and much can be said positively about all these approaches. But other angles in the interaction of people and lepidoptera are receiving increasing attention. As was the case with many of the more memora-

ble lepidopterists of the past, current interest is turning more toward observing behavior. This is becoming the primary activity of increasing numbers of lepidopterists, both professional and amateur.

It is the choice of many people to observe only, and not to do any collecting. They have strong feelings against any collecting that ends in the death of the insect, and they choose never to kill a moth or butterfly, even though it may already have fulfilled its life goals of mating and egg laying and will die a natural death, or be eaten by a natural enemy, within a few days. People who choose this course find no end to the fascination to be obtained, and they are probably more open than anyone else to the opportunities to learn undiscovered facets

103

of insect behavior, which can be far more captivating than the mere beauty of the actors. They are even spared what can become the tedium of properly preparing and protecting a moth or butterfly collection. But in many instances, they cannot be sure what species of insect they have observed or studied. Accurate field identification of free-ranging moths and butterflies can be difficult or impossible, even for experts, particularly with the smaller butterflies and a majority of the moths.

Collecting on film is a partial answer to the problem of verification and identification. A series of close-up photographs of a moth or butterfly, showing the upper and undersurfaces, or of a larva, viewed from above and from the side, may be sufficient for accurate identification. Some pierids and lycaenids habitually rest with their wings closed over their backs, however, so pictures of their upper wing surfaces are nearly impossible to obtain.

But regardless of one's interest in documentation from the scientific point of view, the challenge of photographing a butterfly or moth in the wild far exceeds the challenge of catching it. To catch a butterfly using a 15″ round net on a three or four foot handle is one thing. To "catch" that same butterfly on film—using a camera with a working distance of 9″ to 18″ and a depth of field of less than 1″, with your subject well positioned, using available light, and without blurring motion—is quite another! Anything you can photograph you would have been able to catch with a net. But we have caught many species of butterflies we have not yet succeeded in photographing.

The tendency of the net-swinging collector is to capture the insect at the first opportunity. The time available for be-havior observations is thereby cut short, except for those species with the uncanny ability to gauge just how far a net can reach, and stay about an inch out of range! The photographer, on the other hand, feeling a burning urge to get just one more shot from a better angle or shorter distance, is obliged to observe behavior while attempting to approach the quarry without alarming it. The interaction of a species with others of its kind and with other species can become frustratingly apparent at such a time. Many a beautiful shot is blown at the last instant as the subject dashes off to deal with a presumed rival.

The reward of the successful photographer is a permanent record, often a work of art, which can be shared and enjoyed indefinitely and preserved with little effort. In addition, there is the comforting assurance that no harm has been done, except, at times, to the knees and dignity of the photographer.

It is often convenient and useful to collect on a temporary basis: that is, to collect and carry home live specimens so that more certain identification can be made. Small moths and butterflies can be safely transported singly in vials. Medium or larger butterflies can be carefully placed in glassine envelopes, wings folded over the back, and carried in a small tin box. The insects should be kept in the dark (a knapsack or pants pocket will do) and protected from excessive heat. At home they can be stored for several days at ordinary refrigerator temperature. Chilling the insect reduces its activity temporarily, giving you time to identify it before it becomes warmed up and excited.

Once you have satisfied yourself as to the identity of the specimen, it can be released out of doors, to carry on its activities as if nothing had happened. It is important, however, to release a captured insect in a habitat suitable for its continued survival, and in an area where it normally occurs. Releasing a bog species in an area of old fields or dry upland forest does not allow that individual to resume its normal life-style. Releasing a mated female (and any female caught in the wild must be assumed to have mated) in an area where it has not previously occurred carries the risk of establishing a new population, which can become a pest species. The example of the gypsy moth cannot be overemphasized. Nor should a subspecies from one side of a mountain range be released into the population of a different subspecies on the other side of the range, only fifty or one hundred miles away. The possibility of contaminating a gene pool that has been isolated for thousands of years is a real one, which presents a threat to the resident population.

Rearing lepidoptera, in order to observe and photograph the changes that take place throughout a species' metamorphosis, is a particularly rewarding undertaking, as is rearing unknown caterpillars to maturity so that they can be identified. This involves collecting: garnering eggs found by chance beneath leaves or on twigs and bark, or collected one at a time as you see the ovipositing female place them on her chosen food plant. It can involve capturing adult females, which may then be induced to lay eggs under artificial conditions back home. It can involve collecting larvae and pupae in the field, so that their growth and development can be completed under observation.

Because rearing in captivity can easily result in far higher survival rates than would have occurred in the wild, capturing and collecting a limited number of individuals for this purpose can actually have a positive effect on wild populations, even if only a fraction of a reared brood is released as adults. In contrast to the situation with home-reared birds and mammals, reared lepidoptera are ready to function in the wild as soon as they are released. Their captivity does not result in any conditioning or dependency that would jeopardize their future as free-ranging adults. But all the cautions mentioned with regard to temporary collecting for identification apply here also. Release reared lepidoptera only in appropriate situations.

There is one kind of collecting that can be done with the complete assurance that you are in no way personally reducing the population of any species. This is the collecting of road kills, butterflies either struck by passing motor vehicles, or wind-whipped so severely that they are no longer able to fly. A friend who patrols the roadsides slowly by bicycle has amassed a collection of virtually every butterfly species known to occur in his state, most of them in excellent condition. On some occasions a not-quite-dead female has even produced some eggs, so that he was able to rear the species. We have sometimes picked up excellent specimens in parking lots, where a butterfly, held against the radiator grille of the moving vehicle by wind pressure, had fallen to the ground when the car stopped. There is a problem with data labels in such instances, however. There is no way of knowing how many miles, or hundreds of miles, the butterfly may have been transported, so it is appropriate to add to the label some such notation as "radiator grille" or "parking lot drop."

Moths can also be collected in this manner, but it is not an easy undertaking. They must be searched for at night, or collected at the crack of dawn before the starlings and other avian scavengers come out. Since we prefer to enjoy our lep-watching, we have never tried either of these approaches.

Collecting, then, can range all the way from none at all to collecting for permanent retention of specimens. The decision as to how much or how little collecting to do is an individual one. Anyone can arrive at a decision that is personally comfortable, and at the same time recognize that a different decision on the part of someone else can be accommodated and respected.

CHAPTER 19

Collecting and Children

Figure 19–1 Viceroy and friend

Butterflies are an enigma of sorts. They appear every year, seemingly out of thin air. They come and go with careless élan. They rarely make any sound, and they appear to have no permanent home. Children ask all sorts of questions about them: "How long does a butterfly live?" —"What do butterflies eat?"—"How far can they fly?"—"What is the difference between a butterfly and a moth?"—"Are butterflies poisonous?"—"Will a butterfly die if you rub its wings?"

There are no really clear answers to all these questions. Thousands of species of butterflies exist in the world, and all of them have habits to follow, specific plants that they need, climates in which they can survive, specific seasons for their phases of growth, methods of attracting mates—a seemingly endless

series of requirements and characteristics. But children have a genuine curiosity about these things.

It all began when our oldest child was twelve years old. We were in Maine on the island of Islesboro and were parked beside a patch of undisturbed meadow. Suddenly he burst out of the car with, "Hey! There goes a butterfly!" He catapulted into a maze of wild flowers and returned a moment later with cupped hands. We rolled up all the windows and let the butterfly loose in the car. I had never seen another like it.

We learned the name of the butterfly, a Milbert's tortoise (*Aglais milberti*), from a ragged copy of Holland's *Pocket Butterfly Guide* (1916), found tucked away on the highest shelf. We began to notice other butterflies on the island

and decided to start a collection. Understandably, the two other children also became involved. By summer's end, we had accumulated three shoe boxes full of butterflies, all neatly mounted under scrap glass from the general store, on cotton backed with cardboard and sealed with masking tape, with the names of butterflies and owners on the back. They were not expertly mounted: far from it! But among us we had caught and identified nearly forty species, having looked hardly farther than the boundaries of our own fields. We still have the specimens. For the children, those summers were among the most productive, the most educational, and the most exciting that we can remember. Every new species caught resulted in another wave of enthusiasm.

Toward the end of the second summer, there was an influx of migrating monarchs. For the first time, we noted caterpillars on milkweed. This was when we stopped collecting and turned to rearing. The excitement of watching the incredible changes in the life of this butterfly, the complexity of its metamorphosis, the struggles endured by the little caterpillar as it changed its various skins, and the final triumph as the butterfly emerged, wiped out forever any thought of collecting and killing.

For the children, it was an enrichment. For me, it was the beginning of a career.

The year we reared monarchs was around the time that the monarch banding project began. We had taken some of the caterpillars home to finish rearing them and soon found ourselves part of the tag/release/recover program initiated by Dr. Fred Urquhart in Toronto. The children in the neighborhood began to come and watch, then to come and help. Eventually we took them to see the huge number of monarch butterflies that con-

gregate in Gloucester, Massachusetts, in September on their way to Mexico.

Perhaps the greatest advantage of rearing butterflies is what children can learn about the wonders of life, the respect for nature, and the fragility of small defenseless creatures. Butterflies have many defenses against nature, but few against people. Children who are taught not to kill a butterfly but to admire and respect it will see the world around them in a different light.

Rearing butterflies can be a project for the entire family; it costs little in time and money and provides great rewards. The first step is to find an egg or caterpillar to rear. The monarch is a wonderful beginning butterfly because it is so easily recognized. Its caterpillars, with their yellow, black, and white stripes and their long black "feelers" are unmistakable and are always found on milkweed leaves. They are one of the few butterfly species that keep the same pattern and colors for the entire life of the caterpillar.

One or two monarch caterpillars can be kept in a plastic box (sandwich-size) lined with a damp piece of paper towel. These, a few small milkweed leaves, and a transparent plastic cover, are all that is needed at first. The container needs cleaning and a fresh supply of milkweed daily. A monarch is a voracious feeder. It will moult four times, growing larger with each moult. During its final instar, it may consume as much as five milkweed leaves per day. When full grown, it can be about 1½" long. When it is ready to pupate, stand the box on its side. The caterpillar will want to suspend itself when it sheds its last skin and becomes a chrysalis, and when the butterfly emerges it will need room to stretch its wings.

When we moved to a new town, my husband built a small bay window on the sunny side of the house for the butterflies. I was rearing and photographing life cycles of black swallowtails at that point. One of the neighborhood children who happened to ride by on his bike saw three of the butterflies fluttering against the glass, and before long, an army of children was coming in and out of the house every day. Within a very short time, they began to beg for a butterfly club. They decided that it should be called the Metamorphosis Club. "The little kids are the Caterpillars, and the big kids are the Chrysalids, but Chase and Faith and Dave and the other teenage kids can be the Butterflies."

The Metamorphosis Club was something of a phenomenon.

For an entire year, we spent our spare time with the butterfly. They drew pictures, wrote poetry, and published a weekly newsletter, which one member duplicated on his hand-operated copying machine. It was entitled *Wings over Islington Road*. We went on field trips. We found caterpillars and reared them. The children learned the correct names of their own caterpillars and what food the caterpillars could eat. They fed them every day and reported progress in *Wings*. My husband helped the children make hoops for nets from coat hangers and drilled holes in the ends of sticks to hold the hoops. I helped them make the nets from discarded window curtains and attach them to the handles. Chase, a teenager about to finish high school, made an elaborate butterfly genealogy chart, a virtual masterpiece. David, a potential artist, did a superb drawing of a tiger swallowtail caterpillar.

The whole project was an unplanned operation that would be hard to duplicate. Things were done spontaneously. My husband also designed and cut out parts for small wooden cages that the children nailed together and kept for their own caterpillars. Each cage had a back door that could be raised and lowered or removed, a screened front, and a handle on top for carrying it on field trips. Parents cooperated but did not interfere. They had wisely left us to our own devices but had come to the forefront when help was needed for driving or donating cookies. Any child was welcomed; no one was criticized. Each member reared at least one butterfly and reported progress in the weekly newsletter.

Not a single child would have dreamed of killing a butterfly!

At the end, all parents were invited to an exhibit with refreshments and entertainment. The grand climax was a one-act play. No one but the playwright (Faith, who now works for a television station) and the actors knew what it was to be about. The playwright read it aloud, and the cast acted out the story as she read it. The climax came when a large cardboard box, decorated as a chrysalis, opened at one end and the smallest child emerged wearing monarch wings.

The exhibit included drawings, live specimens in the cages that had been built, copies of the newsletter, and mounted butterflies that had been donated by parents and friends.

The only tragedy occurred when Gwen left her caterpillar in its cage by her open window "so that it could have more sun and fresh air." The city pesticide spray truck came into our street unannounced and sprayed everything in sight. Residue from the sprayer drifted into her room and killed the caterpillar. The reaction of the other members was complete anger and frustration.

Such experiences are a prelude to a way of life. A child learns something of the interdependence of all sorts of living creatures, the need of living creatures to kill in order to survive, as well as their need to protect themselves from being killed. Careful watching can unveil an amazing view of the struggle to survive, of small creatures and their need to protect themselves, whether by hiding, attacking, frightening, or simply being wary. Learning about the lives of moths and butterflies, and the perils that beset them, develops an understanding of the entire natural food chain.

Butterflies have a certain mysterious quality, which arouses all sorts of emotions in people. A collection of butterflies all perfectly mounted and labeled is certainly something to remember, something really remarkable. But to see one live butterfly newly emerged, still unable to fly, to urge it onto a finger and watch it open and close its wings, to discern the patterns and colors of scales, so infinitesimally small and perfect compared to any human handiwork, is really sort of humbling. Rearing one butterfly "from egg to freedom" is an experience that remains a lifelong memory.

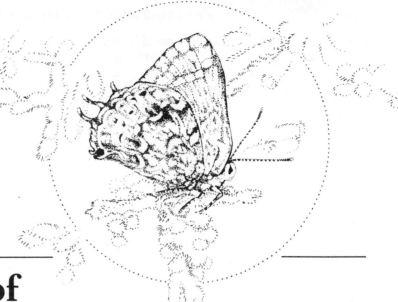

The Role of Amateurs

Figure 20–1 Hessel's hairstreak (*Mitoura hesseli*)

"The amateur and the professional each have much to teach and much to learn from the other, if only some way can be found to bring them together."

It was with words such as these that the Lepidopterists' Society was founded in Cambridge, Massachusetts, in 1947, by two renowned professional lepidopterists. One was the late Harry K. Clench, Curator at the Carnegie Museum of Natural History in Pittsburgh, Pennsylvania. The other was Charles L. Remington, Professor of Biology at Yale University. Both men considered themselves amateurs at the time.

The society that evolved has become a worldwide amalgam of amateur and professional lepidopterists. Its membership listing records the specific interests of every member, whether it be the study of life cycles, collecting, photographing, or the complicated studies of the biology or behavior of various species—even identification of fossil lepidoptera. The only prerequisite for admission is an interest in moths or butterflies.

This all sounds very hospitable, but where do amateurs really fit in?

People become butterfly lovers because of some particular experience that accidentally comes into their lives—an experience perhaps as simple as seeing one butterfly chasing another and trying vainly to follow their instantaneous changes in direction, or perhaps finding a really strange caterpillar, seeing a mating pair of butterflies, or happening upon a small congregation drinking by a mud puddle.

A potential amateur whose curiosity

has been sparked, even by such small events, will think "How?" or "Why?" or "What for?" and from that day on a butterfly will be, for that person, an entity. The next step may be in seeing a strange and interesting caterpillar munching a leaf, and taking it home, leaf and all, and waiting to see what will happen.

The potential amateur lepidopterist will remain interested. Some bright morning there will be a cocoon or chrysalis where the caterpillar had been the day before. All in good time, it will open and suddenly the amateur lepidopterist is no longer "potential."

Once introduced to the life of a butterfly, a person begins to watch for them, read about them, inevitably to admire them, if not to stand in awe of their various actions and life cycles.

People tend to bumble along at first, wishing they had a real lepidopterist to talk with, but most have the feeling that "no real lepidopterist is going to bother with me." One tends to envision the "pros" as being up in their ivory towers reading books full of Latin words or in their labs sorting out butterfly genes.

"And even if I found a real lepidopterist, I wouldn't know what to say, and I would just feel stupid!"

Nothing could be further from the truth. Professional lepidopterists are usually delighted to help you. They want you to see their collections, and they love to tell stories of this or that adventure—and there always are adventures. They want to hear about your experiences. As long as one is engrossed in some aspect of the science, being an amateur really doesn't matter.

All during the nineteenth century there was a tremendous surge of interest in lepidoptera, especially butterflies, both here and abroad. Countless books were written by authors such as F. O.

Morris, H. Noel Humphreys, Henri Fabre, Alpheus S. Packard, Samuel H. Scudder, Thaddeus W. Harris, Henry Edwards, Julia P. Bullard, Mary C. Dickerson, William Kirby, to name but a few. How many people could tell today which were amateurs and which were professionals? Even those who spent a larger part of their time with lepidoptera were still amateurs unless they earned their livings thereby, either from research or from writing. Some were men, some women. Some are recorded as physicians, some as clergymen. A considerable number were well-endowed European gentry, including Lord Rothschild in England and Count Romanoff in Russia.

Reference books regarding life histories of butterflies and moths often give no information as to who worked out these histories. This may be because, again and again, they were worked out by amateurs, whose names have become lost.

The professionals are now aware of what the amateur has to offer, because in his wanderings the amateur may be "in the right place at the right time" to observe happenings that the professional could never "plan" to observe. The professionals are aware of this, and the two groups have come to rely on each other for exchanges of information. Differences in background become obscured by their mutual interests.

A good many of today's professional lepidopterists are specialists, usually with doctorates. If connected with a university, they often must spend a great deal of time in teaching and laboratory work. This frequently involves studying a particular species or group of insects, which may require considerable numbers of specimens from many different locations. Professionals may not have time for such explorations. Such research may also require specimens collected in past years from habitats no longer in existence. For this work, they may rely on the collections of amateurs as much as on those available in museums. For that matter, much of the material now in museums was collected and contributed by amateurs. Diversity in museum collections would often be very limited were it not for these "foot soldiers" of science, whose names remain permanently affixed to the specimens they have procured!

There are amateurs who have carved significant niches for themselves in the economic world. Some write about moths and butterflies. Some raise caterpillars and cocoons to supply to schools, for children to rear as part of the curriculum. Some conduct butterfly tours to various far-off places. Two recent efforts on behalf of the butterfly are the planting of "butterfly gardens" and the building of "butterfly greenhouses."

Considering the large number of species already described, is it possible that there are other species out there waiting to be discovered? In temperate North America, where the physical frontiers have long been eliminated, undescribed species are probably few and are apt to be moths, mostly micro-moths. Nevertheless, in the past forty years, four new species of butterflies have been discovered in the eastern part of the United States: a satyr (*Satyrodes appalachia*), a hairstreak (*Mitoura hesseli*), a blue (*Celastrina ebenina*), and a black swallowtail (*Papilio joanae*). Each of these closely resembles another species long familiar. Careful work by amateurs, or with the help of amateurs, uncovered the differences. There are strong indications that there may be other hidden species among the eastern blues and satyrs, waiting to be discovered by field observations and by rearing.

In the tropics, on the other hand, the number of undescribed species is estimated to be immense. There is evidence that through the destruction of tropical forest habitat, hundreds of species are being driven to extinction each year before they are ever described.

If there is one irrevocable proof of the role for amateurs, it is in the work done for Dr. Fred Urquhart of the University of Toronto by his continentwide team of butterfly banders, which led to the discovery of the monarch roosting sites in Mexico. Vast numbers of amateurs took part in this unique venture. They tagged and released monarchs, which were retrieved sometimes hundreds of miles from the places where they were tagged. These flights were plotted on a map of North America by Dr. Urquhart and his wife, Norah, as the tags were returned. The discovery of the largest colony of overwintering monarchs so far found, sheltering an estimated three to four hundred million monarchs, was made possible by these banders.

The result of this discovery in 1975 has been a concerted effort by amateurs and professionals alike to find a way to preserve the roosting sites. Accomplishing this goal will require not only diplomacy of the highest sort, but also the cooperation of the lumbering industry, which is a major source of employment in Mexico.

In 1971 Robert M. Pyle, then a student at Yale, founded the Xerces Society specifically for the preservation of endangered butterflies and their habitats. It was named for the Xerces blue (*Glaucopsyche xerces*), which became extinct when its habitat in the San Francisco dunes was destroyed by bulldozers in 1943. This organization, also composed of a dedicated mix of amateurs and professionals, has since broadened its scope to the protection of endangered terrestrial arthropods in general.

The most pressing problem now facing not only Xerces, but all lepidopterists, is the protection of the Mexican canyons inhabited by hundreds of millions of monarch butterflies during the winter months. The support of lepidopterists, whether amateur or professional, will be needed to achieve this awesome goal.

In response to this challenge, there has been developed, in conjunction with the Xerces Society, a program called The Monarch Project. Through this program, public support and the energies of all interested conservation organizations will be coordinated in a unified effort to protect the Mexican and Californian over-wintering sites of the monarch butterflies.

The study of lepidoptera is, by its very nature, a source of satisfaction and pleasure to the amateur naturalist. Greater awareness of the biology and the ecological needs of lepidoptera, worked out with the help of alert and curious amateurs, should in the long run prove to be a source of "pleasure and satisfaction" to the moths and butterflies as well.

Monarch butterfly, model (*Danaus plexippus*)

Viceroy, mimic (*Limenitis archippus*)

Pipe vine swallowtail, model (*Battus philenor*)

Spicebush swallowtail, mimic (*Papilio troilus*)

Red spotted purple, mimic (*Limenitis astyanax*)

Black swallowtail female, mimic (*Papilio polyxenes*)

Tiger swallowtail, yellow male (*Papilio glaucus*)

Tiger swallowtail, dark female, mimic

Apollo (*Parnassius apollo*), basking

Hackberry butterfly (*Asterocampa celtis*), perching

American painted lady (*Vanessa virginiensis*), cryptic underside pattern

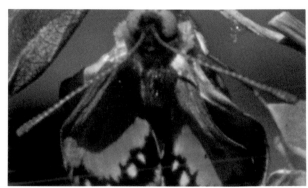
Orange sulphur (*Colias eurytheme*), expanding wings

Dog face butterflies (*Zerene cesonia*), "puddling"

Bronze copper (*Hyllolycaena hyllus*), female, nectaring on knotweed

Compton's tortoise (*Nymphalis vau-album*), feeding on rotting fruit

Tiger swallowtails (*Papilio glaucus*), mating

Mesothea incertata (geometrid), at rest

Operophtera bruceata (geometrid), male mating with wingless female

Olive angle shades, (*Phlogophora iris*), in cryptic resting position

New England buck moth (*Hemileuca lucina*), flying male about to mate with calling female

Cecropia moth (*Hyalophora cecropia*)

Primrose moth (*Schinia florida*), resting in blossom of common evening primrose

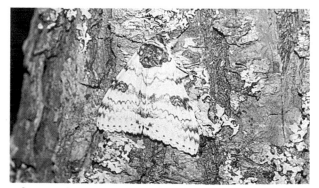

White underwing (*Catocala relicta*), in resting position

Once-married underwing (*Catocala unijuga*), feeding at bait

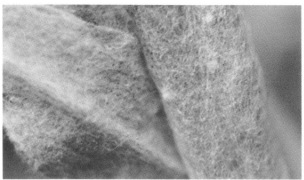
Eggs of American painted lady (*Vanessa virginiensis*), concealed in fuzz on leaves of pearly everlasting

Chrysalis of American painted lady

Larva of hollow-spotted plagodis (*Plagodis alcoolaria*), camouflaged as an oak twig

Larva of double-toothed prominent (*Nerice bidentata*), on elm leaf

Larva of *Automeric zephyria*, relative of the io moth, showing stinging spines

Larva of viceroy (*Limenitis archippus*) constructing hibernaculum

California tent caterpillars (*Malacosoma californicum*), working on tent

Prepupal larva of black swallowtail (*Papilio polyxenes*) making "seat belt"

CHAPTER 21

Is Collecting Harmful?

Figure 21–1 Bay checkerspot (*Oxydryas editha*)

Collecting, in the sense of capturing and preserving individual insects so that they can be retained permanently, is a regular practice among lepidopterists. Is collecting harmful? That is, does collecting jeopardize the overall opportunity for a species to reproduce and maintain its numbers year after year? Does collecting compromise the ability of a particular population of butterflies to survive? While the answer is generally "no," it is not inevitably "no." What are the considerations?

Among cold-blooded vertebrates, the care bestowed by parents on offspring varies from zero to very elaborate attention. For warm-blooded vertebrates, parental care is an absolute necessity for the survival of their young. Such is not the case with lepidoptera. The female but-

terfly exercises great care in selecting the proper plant on or near which to place her eggs, and she may also take care in placing the eggs in locations that will reduce the chances of their being discovered by predators or parasites. Moths behave similarly, and some take the additional precaution of covering a mass of eggs with hairs removed from the maternal abdomen. Whether this serves as camouflage, as a temperature buffer, or a deterrent to predation is not clear. However, depositing the eggs ends the female's involvement with her offspring. She makes no further attempt to assure their survival by controlling temperature, furnishing shelter, providing food, or protecting them from predators. The male's interest ended once he provided the female with sperm for fertiliz-

115

ing her ova. The lepidopteran egg is on its own.

Collecting for specimens, then, does not jeopardize the survival of offspring, once eggs have been laid. To what extent can collecting compromise egg laying?

Most female moths remain close to the places where they emerge until they have attracted mates and finished mating. In order to avoid attracting attention from predators during this vulnerable period, they tend to remain as obscure and quiet as possible. Egg laying begins usually within a few hours after completion of mating. Some moths lay their eggs in batches and finish the job within a day or two. Some spread the process out over a number of days, as more eggs gradually mature. Among the butterflies, a few species "batch" their eggs, but most fly about a great deal, laying them singly or in small groups in carefully selected locations. The heliconian butterflies, such as the zebra butterfly in Florida, are an extreme example: the females live for many months and deposit their eggs very sparingly. It is clear that the earlier in her career such a female is captured, the fewer eggs she will have left behind her.

When collecting free-flying moths and butterflies, or when using lights to attract them, one notices that with most species the number of males captured is far in excess of the number of of females. Specimens collected while they are "mud-puddling" are almost exclusively males. When baits are used as attractants, the opposite may be true, and mostly females are taken. This is particularly true of some genera of tropical butterflies, where a few baited traps can capture most of a local female population.

Removing males from a population is much less significant than removing females. Males generally emerge a few days earlier than females, so each emerg-

ing female finds a good supply of males ready and waiting. In addition, males are eager and able to mate with more than one female, so removal of a considerable number of males does not put the females at risk of going unfertilized. In those species of butterflies in which the males use territorial patrolling or perching as a means of mate location, a territory that has its male captured is quickly reoccupied by another male that had a less satisfactory territory or none at all.

For the many species of lepidoptera that occupy extensive habitats, collecting is not a significant hazard. The individual moths and butterflies move about a great deal from one locality to another. Removing a few individuals has no more general effect than dipping cupfuls of water from a flowing stream. And collectors are just one more type of predator, usually far less numerous and far less efficient than the natural predators. The females have been coping with this problem since their origin in the geologic past. If only two of the hundreds of eggs laid by each reach maturity, the population will remain stable.

The story is quite different for species that occupy very restricted habitats, such as small bogs, isolated canyons, or places where a very limited stand of the larval food plant occurs. Such species often have very little movement from one colony to another. Here it can be possible for a skilled and determined collector to capture virtually all the individuals in a population and to cause that population severe or even permanent damage, particularly if the collecting is done just at the time most of the females have emerged.

In general, if a rather small number of individuals of any species is collected, and the emphasis is on males, the future of the population will not be jeopardized. Many species of butterflies fly about while copulating, especially if disturbed. These couples, which have not yet embarked on their egg-laying careers, should not be collected.

Since sex is important when collecting, how are we to tell male butterflies and moths from females? In some species, the males and females have different patterns or colors (they are sexually dimorphic), as is the case with many of the swallowtails and sulphurs. Others have "sex scales" (androconia) on the wings of the males: patches or folds containing specialized scales found only on males. The black dot on a hind wing vein of the monarch, and the dark or metallic "stigmata" on the forewings of the "branded skippers," are examples. The field guides point out these differences. Very often the female may be larger or more robust than the male or have a slightly different wing shape, such as more rounding of the outer corner (apex) of the forewing. With many moths the antennae of the males are heavier, or more coarsely notched, or more feathery than those of the female. When the two sexes are viewed together, these differences can be very striking. The abdomen of the female, because of its content of eggs, is likely to be bigger and heavier than that of the male, sometimes to a marked degree. The most reliable difference, however, is in the shape of the tip of the abdomen. The undersurface of the male abdomen usually shows a fore-and-aft slit where the two claspers, used in mating, come together. This can be very obvious in some families, such as swallowtails, and much less so in others, as in some of the subfamilies of nymphalids. In some moths, this feature may be obscured by long hair at the end of the abdomen. This difference is usually difficult to use for field identification, so

that the individual must often be captured and inspected in order to determine its sex.

The key to safe collecting, then, is restrained collecting. Moths and butterflies should be collected only with a specific purpose in mind, not just "because they are there." The number collected from a particular species should also be purposeful. The average person collecting for personal interests has no need for dozens or hundreds of a single species, nor is he likely to have the space to store them and care for them properly. We have seen collectors with a net in each hand, taking butterflies so fast that every specimen was damaged. This is simply unthinking greed. The collector who tells us that he stopped collecting after the first few hundred specimens of one species, because his arm got too sore, is only to be condemned. This is obviously not restrained collecting, but collecting that should be restrained.

When collecting is carried out with such avidity as this, the goal is usually not scientific or personal, but commercial. Specimens of newly discovered species, species proposed for listing as threatened or endangered, or species occurring in remote and limited habitats that are difficult to reach can be sold for inflated prices to those who collect lepidoptera after the manner of stamp collectors. These are species of which little or no collecting should be done.

A few species of lepidoptera have been listed by the federal or various state governments as endangered, usually because their very small remaining populations are based on very limited and fragile habitats. It goes without saying that these species must not be collected or interfered with at any stage of their development. Species listed as threatened, or proposed for listing in either category, should be similarly respected. Local offices of The Nature Conservancy may be the best place to find information about these listings, since they supply much of the input when a species is being considered for listing. When in doubt, just don't collect; the law makes no allowance for ignorance. Page 175 contains a list of the species classified by the federal government as endangered at the time this book was written.

Recently the Lepidopterists' Society, in response to a survey of its members, put together a concise set of guidelines for the collection of lepidoptera. Adherence to these guidelines will keep collecting within limits that will not jeopardize healthy populations, but that will allow appropriate collecting for scientific and educational purposes and for personal pleasure.

These guidelines are reprinted in full beginning on page 177. They should be read by all lepidoptera-watchers, whether collecting or not, since they have important bearing on the protection of butterfly habitats.

The real enemy to the survival of butterfly and moth species is not the collecting activities of humans, but our ignorant or unthinking activities that result in the destruction of necessary habitat. The Xerces blue and a subspecies of the satyrid *Cercyonis sthenele* disappeared forever when their sand dune habitat was overwhelmed by the foundations and pavement of San Francisco. As already described, the large blue disappeared from England under most ironic circumstances, as researchers were trying to learn enough about its biology to protect it.

The importance of critical habitat, and all its component species, cannot be overstated.

CHAPTER 22

Commerce in Lepidoptera

Figure 22–1 A birdwing butterfly (*Trogonoptera brookiana*) in display case

The subject of commerce in lepidoptera really has little to do with a book for amateur naturalists on observing butterflies and moths. It is included here in order to broaden the perspective of the place held by lepidoptera in the world at large.

There are many people, particularly teachers dealing with children, who wish to purchase cocoons of the larger American silkmoths to use as classroom teaching aids. Fortunately there are a few people scattered about the country, often amateurs who enjoy rearing caterpillars, or who collect cocoons in the wild, who are able to meet this need. People benefit, and the species do not suffer; no cocoon collector is close to 100 percent efficient, nor will he want to collect enough to jeopardize the crop for next year.

There is also commerce in adult moths and butterflies, which can be purchased folded and dried, in paper envelopes. Some of these are used by teachers for teaching aids. They are also sought by collectors who want examples of species from areas to which they are unable to travel themselves; armchair collectors make up a good part of this market. Unfortunately, since the demand is frequently for rare species, these may be intensively collected and their survival thereby compromised.

Another type of collecting, which might be termed "contract collecting," may be done at the behest of someone who is trying to build a reference or research collection of lepidoptera for a museum. Or a researcher may engage local collectors to sample the species in a particular area in order to determine whether intensive study may be fruitful. This has been as important a source of material for museums as have been the collections of amateurs.

In Papua New Guinea, butterfly farming for commercial sale has been developed. The programs are under careful government control and provide a livelihood to the workers staffing the farms. The subjects are mainly the huge and strikingly beautiful birdwing butterflies (fig. 22–1), many of which are endangered or threatened. Because a portion of the crop is returned to the wild, populations are enhanced rather than jeopardized.

In other countries, numbers of people are employed to collect butterflies for use in the production of artifacts: specimens embedded in plastic for anything from paper weights to toilet seats; pictures made of montages of detached butterfly wings; single or grouped specimens displayed for their beauty alone. These artifacts provide a living for the collectors and for the producers of the handicrafts, and they usually utilize species that breed prolifically in areas already disturbed by human activities. Feelings run high as to the appropriateness of the use of butterflies for these purposes, but the issues are not as clear-cut as was the case with egret plumes in the last century. While we are not generally in sympathy with the use of lepidoptera in artifacts, we cannot deny that the beauty of a tiny blue butterfly in a tastefully crafted pendant far outclasses that of the most expensive gem.

These issues are addressed in the Statement of the Committee on Collecting Policy of The Lepidopterists' Society, reprinted beginning on page 177.

PART V

Tricks and Tools

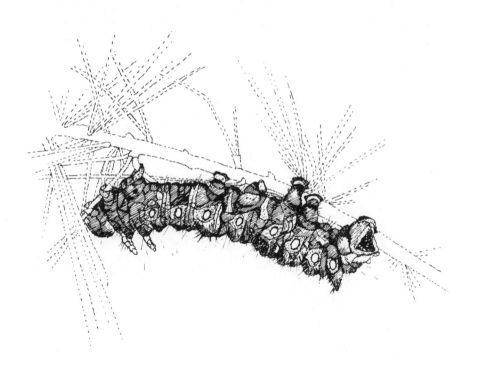

23

Notes and Data Records

Wandering about in the woods and fields can be most pleasant. You watch butterflies and moths feeding, basking, evading birds. You look for caterpillars and see wasps and flies looking for them. You observe things you have read about in books, or variations on what is written, not to mention behaviors that may be quite contradictory to what the books have led you to expect. You discuss your observations later in the day with interested friends, the details clear in your mind. Next week you discuss them with other friends, but the details are becoming a bit blurred. Was that larva on ash or elm; was the yellow stripe on the back or the side? Was it the female or the male of that mated pair that was doing the flying?

When it comes to reinforcing one's own recollections, and for that matter, one's credibility, there is no substitute for field notes. If it is possible to refer to a notebook, with data on the date, place visited, and weather and temperature conditions, as well as the species observed and details worthy of record, little will be lost but doubt.

The manner of notekeeping will vary with the interest and perhaps with the compulsiveness of the individual. It is often handy to carry a small pocket notebook in which a few cryptic comments can be recorded in the field. If this can be formalized each day into a diary type of ledger, retrieval in a chronological fashion will be easy. Transfer of details to cards for filing by species, by larval food plants, by nectar sources, and so forth may serve specific purposes. Keeping track of numbers on a rough log scale—such as 1–2, 2–5, 5–10, 10–20, 50–100—can simplify comparison of prevalence of a species from place to place, day to day, or season to season. If you are rearing larvae of unknown identity found in the wild, it is helpful to give the individual a reference number, against which are recorded locality, food plant, estimated stage of development, and the date on which it was found. A color photograph, keyed with the same reference number, is invaluable in refreshing future recollections of the specimen, especially if a new photograph is taken as the larva's appearance changes on subsequent moults. The number serves as positive identification of the specimen as it goes through its pupal stage in its individual emergence cage. Mixing of identity at this stage can ruin an otherwise successful rearing. Moth pupae in particular have few memorable "field marks," and a few species mixed together without proper labeling quickly lose their identity, and the notes and photographs lose much of their value.

If you are on a trip where there is

much to be seen and little time for note taking, a small, lightweight recorder can be a great boon. Transferring your notes to paper later on, however, can be quite a chore.

The fashion in which notes are kept is an individual matter; yet regardless of their form, two things are essential: they should be recorded soon enough to be completely accurate, and they should be organized or filed so that desired information can be readily found again.

Data labeling has certain minimum requirements: the place and date that the specimen was photographed or collected, and the name of the photographer or collector. This information is written on the frame of a transparency, on the margin or back of a print, or on the label of the vial, envelope, or pin of every preserved specimen. The identity of the species should be added if and when it becomes known, but on a separate label in the case of pinned specimens. Identification can be incorrect and need to be changed, whereas place, date, and collector are unalterable facts.

How should place be indicated? A convenient routine is to use province or state, county, and locality. The first can be spelled out, or abbreviated in some conventional fashion—the two-letter postal abbreviation may be used. County name is best spelled out, as : "Suffolk Co." Locality should include at least a town name as shown on a road map, or a distance from an identified intersection, or approximate distance and bearing from a named feature on a geodetic survey map. Local names such as Higgins Farm or Bailey's Creek may convey little or no information ten or one hundred years later, but a properly labeled photograph or specimen can have value far longer than that. For mountainous areas, a statement of approximate altitude in feet or meters can be valuable information.

It is important to record dates in an unambiguous and uniform manner. The date 5–8–85 may mean 5 August to me and May 8 to you. The use of 5 VIII 85 or 5 Aug 85 removes all doubt. This follows the international system, where the units proceed from smaller to larger: day, month, year. The spelled abbreviation for the month, rather than the Roman numeral, reads more easily, especially on a small label beneath the body of an insect.

The name of the collector should be as simple as "J. B. Smith, Coll."

In addition to these absolute necessities, other bits of information can be useful, such as situation or manner of collecting: "at bait," "at carrion," "nectaring at (species of flower)," "MV" (mercury vapor light), "BL" (blacklight), "day" (for a moth flying in the daytime), etc. Reared specimens, which often emerge outside the regular flight period, shoud be labeled "ex ovo," "ex larva," or "ex pupa," according to the stage at which you started caring for the insect. But there is a limit to what can be included. Labels must be small, and they must be readable. It is possible to inscribe the Gettysburg Address on the head of a pin, but it does not communicate well. At the other extreme, a "barn-door" label, which tells all that can possibly be told, is unwieldy and can damage adjacent specimens.

A resplendent black, green, and gold birdwing butterfly from New Guinea, in the Museum of Comparative Zoology at Harvard University, bears a barn-door label that does seem justifiable, however. It reads: "I sent you the one and only *Ornithoptera paradisea* it was ever my good fortune to receive. Karl V. Hagen, who took this pair, was afterwards eaten by the Papuans, and the only thing he left his wife was about four pairs of these, and I believe Staudinger received them. At any rate, when I wanted a pair for a customer, a year or two ago, I wrote to him, and as you will see by the enclosed, he had some. I thought £20 was too much to give to re-sell at a profit, I think you will agree you get them cheap for (virtually) £14/10." (This is not to suggest, to be sure, that the average North American lep-watcher needs to be looking constantly over his shoulder!)

There is a particular caution about specimens reared from immature stages. The locality recorded must be that of the locality where the immature stage, or its parent, was collected or originated in the wild, not that of the locality where the adult insect was reared or emerged. If the larva of a subtropical species collected in Florida produces a moth while I am vacationing in Maine, and I label it "Maine," the data on that specimen becomes worthless, and the data on all my reared material loses credibility. It is the sort of error for which a number of otherwise excellent lepidopterists have become infamous.

The crux of the data matter is simple. A photograph or a specimen without reliable data attached to it may be pretty, but it is pretty worthless.

CHAPTER
24

Photography

To cover all the aspects of photography of butterflies and moths would require not only a whole book, but more skill and experience than we can muster. Each lepidopterist tends to settle on methods with which she or he is most comfortable. These methods evolve over time as more effective equipment becomes available at reasonable prices, and as new ideas are picked up from colleagues. This account describes approaches that we have found workable and satisfying.

There are basic needs to consider. The camera and any accessory equipment should be easy to carry, so that the equipment itself is not a source of fatigue throughout a long, hot day in the field. We have always tried to avoid having the camera put any restraints on our mobility or durability. In addition, the camera should be as unobtrusive as possible. Some types of lens covers that dangle from the lens when you are using the camera can easily spook your subject, as may broad side brackets bearing accessory flashes.

Because many butterflies tend to stay in one place only briefly, even when they are not alarmed, the camera may need to be used quite quickly. If a lot of time is required to determine shutter speed and aperture, as well as to frame your subject and focus, you will photo-graph a lot of nice flowers but rather few butterflies. It is also desirable to be able to produce a large enough image on the film for the butterfly to fill a third or half the width of the frame. At the same time, this has to be accomplished without having to approach the subject so closely as to frighten it away. Exposures need to be short enough so that a small amount of motion will not be a problem. Some butterflies tend to move about a bit or to fan their wings as they feed or perch, as, for example, the back and forth motion of a hairstreak's hind wings. Even the flowers move; it is a rare day when there is not at least a little breeze at just the wrong time.

Last of the basics is protection of your investment in camera and lens. A conventional leather camera case is clumsy in the field. An ordinary neck strap is fine, but you will need to keep one hand on the camera to keep it from banging against rocks if you bend or kneel down to look at something. If you are collecting and photographing on the same trip, you may need two free hands.

There are several workable solutions to this problem. A Kuban Hitch®, a special strap going around the chest and over the shoulders, which uses a pair of heavy rubber bands to hold the camera firmly against the chest wall, is very satisfactory, at least for males. The camera does not bounce about, and it can be used very quickly. Its drawback is steady pressure on the ridge of the shoulder, which can become quite tiring after a few hours. A widely advertised device is a circular chest strap bearing a velcro patch that grips an opposing patch cemented to the back of the camera. (The camera is supported by a conventional neck strap.) This is fairly effective, but when we have used it, we have found that the patches may separate unpredictably if we bend over. Our current preference is for a "pistol-grip" handle screwed into the camera's tripod socket. We remove the cable release from the grip, and tuck the handle inside a trouser belt (fig. 24–1). The camera is instantly available, yet stays in place when not in use.

With no camera case, the inevitable shower must be kept in mind. A plastic bag of appropriate size, adequately closeable, is an absolute necessity. A haze filter (which does not compromise either exposure time or color values) can protect the outer surface of your lens from unwelcome encounters with grit and twigs.

Choice of camera is a very personal matter, which usually includes consideration of the other purposes for which the camera will be used. In any case, a single lens reflex (SLR) camera is most commonly useful, since it gives absolute accuracy in framing the subject. If the SLR camera you use also has through-the-lens (TTL) metering, then accurate exposure control can be quickly attained. A more recent development utilizing TTL metering, often called programmed exposure, automatically adjusts the shutter speed and/or the lens aperture, leaving you with no other tasks than to frame the subject and focus the lens. Automatic focusing is an advance with

which we have had no experience. Because of limited field depth, the critical matter of focusing seems best left to the photographer! Automatic film advance is another development we have not yet adopted. It adds a small amount of weight to the camera, which is no advantage. Whether its sound is sufficient to spook butterflies, we do not know. At times even the sound of your camera's shutter will be enough to put your subject to flight.

Some SLR cameras offer a choice of focusing screens. A split-image screen is generally standard. It allows critically sharp focusing on a linear detail of the subject, such as a wing vein or margin, an antenna, or a bristle. For some people, these screens have the annoying drawback of having one half of the split image "black out" if the operator's eye gets just a trifle out of line with the optical axis of the finder. This phenomenon

Figure 24–1 Use of "pistol-grip" attachment for carrying camera

is accentuated with shorter working distances and with lenses of longer focal length. It can be overcome with practice. Screens with a complete matte field, or with a central microprism focusing spot, avoid this problem, but they are a little harder to focus critically. A little trying before buying may be worthwhile.

With the immense proliferation of lenses now available, making a choice or choices may seem increasingly difficult. Since the subjects in which the lepwatcher is interested are often very small, a lens with "macro" capacity is highly desirable. This designation means that the lens can be focused from infinity down to a working distance so short that the image recorded on the film can be as large as one quarter to one half natural size. With such a lens, it is easy to take both habitat shots and close-ups without need for changing lenses. Some of these lenses are zooms, with quite a variety of focal-length ranges. The zooms, however, usually give images only one quarter natural size at maximum; they weigh a good deal more than plain macro lenses, and the maximum aperture is somewhat smaller, resulting in reduced usefulness in dim light.

Our preference has been for the plain macro lenses: the 50 mm macro weighing less than half a pound, with a minimum working distance of about nine inches for a half-natural-size image, and the 100 mm macro, weighing about 14 ounces, with the minimum working distance a little under eighteen inches. The longer lens with its longer working distance, while clumsier to handle, spooks fewer butterflies and is also very beneficial for photographers whose backs are not too flexible! Both these lenses include a "life-size" adapter, an extension tube allowing increase in image size to 1:1. While these extension tubes are

rather clumsy for use in the field, they are extremely useful for photographing small larvae in their early instars.

Choice of film is another important detail. You will need to decide whether you will usually wish to see your photographs as transparencies for projection, prints for viewing in hand, or both. Prints can be made from slides, and slides from color-print negatives, but the processing is unfortunately expensive. Motion picture film, processed for either medium, can prove quite inexpensive.

The familiar 25 and 64 ASA films give excellent results, both as to color values and fineness of grain, but these films call for very good light and very quiet, cooperative subjects. One can only use shutter speeds of 60 or 125, with a fairly large aperture (and hence reduced depth of field). Here again motion picture films, ranging from 200 to 640 ASA (or even 1200 ASA with special processing), make possible the use of faster shutter speeds and smaller apertures, with better control over motion and depth of field. We have found that these films tend to favor the blue end of the spectrum and are weaker with the red than are the 25 and 64 ASA transparency films. In some respects this makes them a little less "pretty" but a little more lifelike. Truly blue butterflies are honestly rendered. Conventional transparency films with speeds higher than 64 ASA have been available for some time, but when we have tried them in the past, they have seemed undesirably grainy. The only useful general advice is to test out various sorts of film and choose the type that serves and pleases you best.

The use of supplemental lighting is a subject that can inspire heated discussion among amateur insect photographers. There is no question that the use of flash can yield butterfly photographs of intense clarity, superb color quality, and excellent depth. This is demonstrated by several of the most recent butterfly books, which use photographs for species identification. Yet in many cases these butterflies appear silhouetted against black backgrounds, which many people, including ourselves, look upon as unnatural and aesthetically distasteful. Butterflies, while beautiful in themselves against a black background (or on a pin in a box), are most commonly seen in a naturally lighted setting, as part of a larger scene. Our preference is to try to capture them in that scene, as we see them, using available light. Even with the faster films and carefully controlled exposure, this means some sacrifice of clarity of background, but the effect on the viewer is that of looking in upon the butterfly as it goes about its business, rather than that the butterfly has been plucked and brought to the viewer. We prefer to reserve flash for supplemental lighting in obscure situations, such as a butterfly at roost or a concealed caterpillar. With moths, of course, it is a different matter. It is usually a case of flash or no picture. Even recording the resting postures of moths in the daytime may call for supplemental flash, since they tend to pick resting places in the dimmest light possible. When you use supplemental flash, a system that meters the flash automatically through the lens can go a long way toward avoiding unnaturally black backgrounds.

When life histories are being studied, photography is an excellent way to record the details of the egg and of each larval instar. Posturing habits and patterns of communal feeding are also easily recorded. While photographs in natural settings would be ideal, this is often difficult to manage and still have adequate light and positioning to illustrate all the desired details. Therefore the use of a neutral background against which to photograph a caterpillar resting on its food plant is a useful practice. The color should differ from that of the caterpillar for good contrast but should be neither very light nor very dark, so as not to compromise proper exposure of the larva. We use medium gray, tan, and olive green. Velvetlike flocked cloth that has no discernible fabric pattern is excellent.

Eggs and the earliest instar larvae may be so small that the use of the extension tube for a 1:1 image is still not quite adequate. If you are seriously interested in recording these stages, excellent images up to a ratio of about 3.8:1 can be obtained using an appropriate bellows and an ordinary 50 mm lens, and as high as 8:1 using a wide-angle lens mounted backward by means of a "reversing ring." Such work requires a considerable amount of practice and experimentation with your particular equipment in order to achieve proper exposure and lighting.

The subject of lighting brings up a caution to be considered. Rather few larvae feed in full sunlight on the tops of leaves. To do so increases their exposure to the risk of predation. It also increases the risk of overheating form absorption of too much sunlight, particularly if the larva is dark-colored. While the use of sunlight for photographing larvae can give excellent clarity and detail, many larvae, when placed unprotected in the sun, become immediately agitated and seek shelter beneath a leaf. This behavior should be respected, and even anticipated if the larvae are small, a fact we had tragically impressed upon us on one occasion.

In a canyon in Wyoming, we had the good fortune to find one egg of the western tiger swallowtail (*Papilio rutulus*) and one of the pale swallowtail (*P. eury-medon*), species we had never had the opportunity to rear. Back at home, both eggs hatched the same day, and we started to take what we intended to be a series of comparative pictures of their life histories. We placed each tiny black larva on a leaf of its food plant, in the sun. As we were focusing, each larva began to race rapidly toward the edge of its inchwide leaf. They were stopped dead in their tracks, overheated by the sun's rays. They had been needlessly killed.

CHAPTER
25

Collecting Equipment

The basic and most familiar piece of collecting equipment used by lepidopterists is the hand net. No cartoonist would ever portray a collector without one. While you can occasionally entice a butterfly onto your finger, gently pluck one from a flower between thumb and forefinger, or pop a jar over one, repeated success in capturing moths and butterflies depends on skillful use of a net. The net increases your reach, moves very quickly when you need it to, and most important, when properly handled, it makes it possible for you to capture the insect without injuring it.

The usual design of the net is a circular hoop fixed to a lightweight handle. The hoop carries a cylindrical or somewhat conical mesh net bag, rounded at the bottom and two and a half to three times as long as the diameter of the hoop. The fabric should be small-meshed, as for mosquito netting, and made of durable synthetic fibers that are reasonably soft. Polyester netting meets these requirements very well. The open end of the bag, which is attached to the hoop, is usually made of, or reinforced with, muslin for increased durability. We prefer a material that is dyed a dark color, such as olive or gray, rather than white, on the assumption that this will be less obvious to the insects, but many

people seem to feel that this is not a significant point.

Nets can be purchased in various sizes and weights, with short or long handles, even collapsible so that they will fit easily into a pocket, backpack, or suitcase. Many collectors, however, are inclined to make their own equipment, which allows for any sort of variation that may suit their fancies. A very useful, inexpensive, and easily handled homemade net can be constructed from a wire coat hanger formed into a hoop, taped to a bamboo stake about a yard long (black friction tape works well), and fitted with a mesh bag as previously described. While such a net may be only eleven inches in diameter, it is very serviceable and is good for a starter. One of the nets we use most has an old telescoping aluminum tripod leg for a handle, with a 15″ hoop of fairly heavy wire. This handle can be conveniently shortened or extended, depending on the reach required. For high work in the tops of small trees, we use an extensible aluminum pole designed for painting stairwells with a roller brush; an 18″ diameter collapsible commercial net can easily be taped to the end of the pole, giving an additional 12′ of extended reach.

The stereotypical cartoon of the collector racing wildly across a field in hot pursuit of a receding butterfly illustrates the least efficient manner of using a net and one of the quickest ways of breaking a leg in a chuckhole. And the frantic collector will rush past, and disturb, any number of things worth looking at. Our preferred approach is to watch the bug for a bit to see what is going on, photograph it if it is a worthy specimen or doing something worth recording, and then catch it if it is necessary to have a better look at it for identification, to use it for obtaining eggs, or to retain it permanently.

Catch it how? In order to avoid damaging both the insect and the plant on which it is resting, the best approach, if the plant is no taller than the length of the net, is to hold the tail of the net in one hand and with the other to lower the hoop quickly down over the plant, right to the ground, without letting go of the end of the bag. The enclosed insect will usually fly up to the top of the bag. It is then an easy matter, with a little practice, to raise the net and quickly rotate the handle 180° so the net folds over upon itself and the insect is trapped in the far end. If the plant is taller, the best approach is to sweep the insect from its perch with a quick flick of the wrist (a backhand stroke is very effective), taking care not to decapitate the flower in the process. Again, a quick rotation of the handle will fold the net bag and trap the insect in the far end. A butterfly on a tree trunk can be a particular challenge, but it can often be picked off by a carefully gauged flick of the net. An insect on the ground can be taken by popping the net down over it, holding the end of the bag up as before. Holding the bag is particularly important when a butterfly is enjoying one of the more unsavory sites of which some species are so fond, such as carrion, feces, or a barnyard puddle. If

the netting collapses into the muck, the butterfly may get fouled up, and the net will require a good washing and drying before it can be used again. You must also be particularly careful when using the net near roses, brambles, catbrier, and barbed wire; a ripped net can dampen your day as much as a heavy rain.

A few groups of butterflies, such as some of the elfins and some arctics, use a tactic that sorely challenges the collector. When you clap your net down over one of these creatures, it may remain undisturbed and refuse to fly up into the net. It then walks deliberately about and escapes at a point where the rim of the net fails to make close contact with the uneven surface of the ground. And in the case of the arctics, which often alight on jumbled piles of rocks, your quarry will slowly amble down between the rocks to a place where it would take a crowbar to expose it. We can only applaud the actions of such individuals.

In some species the males search for mates by "patrolling." They may fly a zigzag course back and forth across a field, or follow a circular route about the edge of a wood or along woodland paths or streams. If you stand and wait, you may discover that a single individual will pass a particular spot, always from the same direction, at regular intervals of perhaps five or ten minutes. Waiting and executing a carefully timed swing may make it possible to snare the insect, but the swing should not be so vigorous as to be damaging. Because their eyes are so well designed for detecting objects in motion, butterflies have an uncanny ability to dodge slightly, pass beside or beneath the moving net, and continue on their patrols undisturbed. A swing from beneath and behind the insect, as it goes past, may therefore be more successful.

Once you have a moth or butterfly in the net, how can you deal with it without damaging it? Commonly, if the insect has relatively large wings in proportion to body size, it is possible to flatten the net about it so that the wings are folded up over the back and it becomes quiet. You can then immobilize it by gently grasping the sides of the thorax, from outside the net, with thumb and forefinger. Then reach inside the net with the other hand and grasp the insect directly with thumb and forefinger, always by the sides of the thorax, not by the wings themselves. Holding a moth or butterfly by the wings will dislodge scales and cause irreparable damage. Once the insect is in hand it can be slipped into a small envelope (of a sort to be described later), with the wings still folded over the back, and carried in a rigid box in a dark place.

Skipper butterflies and moths with relatively small wings and large bodies are usually stimulated into frantic buzzy activity when enclosed in a net, and if you attempt to restrain them with your fingers you will often damage them severely. Small plastic vials, such as pill vials, or glass jars with easily handled lids offer the best way to deal with such insects. I remove the cover and hold it in my teeth, reach inside the net with the open vial, maneuver it over the insect, and cap the vial temporarily with my fingers. With a little luck the cover can be replaced without losing or damaging the captive. I then put the vial into a dark pocket or carrying bag, where the insect sits quietly and travels safely. Put only one insect into each vial. Two will continually stimulate each other into flight, and both will be badly damaged.

Small lycaenid butterflies, such as elfins, coppers, blues, and hairstreaks, and small geometrid moths, while they have relatively large wings and small bodies, are so delicate that it is difficult to handle them safely with the fingers. I prefer to use the vial method for removing them from the net and transporting them.

CHAPTER 26

Carrying Equipment

If it is your choice to do more than just observe, record, and photograph as you go on your lep-watching excursions, that is, if you plan to collect some specimens to bring home for rearing or further study, a bit of simple equipment is a necessity. To collect a specimen and be unable to carry it satisfactorily, so as to avoid damage or death, is wasteful and frustrating. Segregation of individual adult specimens to reduce agitation is necessary, as mentioned before. Segregation of larvae by species is advantageous, to avoid food plant mix-ups, and to avoid having one species attack and eat another.

Small glassine envelopes or paper coin envelopes are useful for carrying the more robust butterflies, placed in the envelope with the wings folded together over the back. While a shirt pocket may seem a convenient place to carry such a specimen, it has its disadvantages. Shirt pockets often empty themselves when you bend over to examine something on the ground, and perspiration can soak into the envelope and damage the specimen, even if you take the precaution of placing a plastic card behind the envelopes. Also, an accidental bump into something solid can crush the insects. For these reasons, it is better to have a rigid (but not airtight) box in which the envelopes can be loosely stacked; the box should be transported in a dark pocket or knapsack where the specimens cannot become overheated. Metal Band-Aid cans are excellent for this purpose.

Pill vials of various sizes are extremely useful for carrying skippers and small and delicate butterflies and moths. A small belt pouch filled snugly enough with vials so they won't tumble about is excellent for carrying these. The vials are useful also for transporting small larvae, with a sprig of the food plant, and for any eggs you happen to find. As with the envelopes, the occupied vials should be kept in the dark and protected from overheating. While a small butterfly or a few small larvae do not ordinarily consume enough oxygen to suffocate in an airtight vial in a period of four to five hours, there is no harm in loosening the lid for a moment now and then to change the air. Using perforated vials is not the answer, at least for caterpillars, as the food plant will dry out rapidly and small larvae will escape through the holes.

It is very handy to carry a few extra metal or plastic boxes in a belt pack, to simplify carrying larger larvae or numbers of smaller ones. Such containers are also useful to protect cocoons and pupae from crushing during transport.

Since you never know when you may wish to transport a large amount of vegetation, such as a whole colony of communally feeding, nest-forming larvae, or a week's supply of a food plant not available close to home, a supply of empty plastic bags can be invaluable. Plain bags, which can be closed with wire twists, are very satisfactory, and it is easy to carry several filled ones between your fingers, holding them by the necks. "Zip-locs" have the advantage of being tougher and can be blown up quite easily before being sealed, but they are rather clumsy to carry in the field once they are filled. It is a good idea, when possible, to take filled bags back to a car where they can be stowed in a closed trunk, or in a carton placed beneath the car, in the shade and protected from being blown away by the wind. Never store livestock within a closed car, as the "greenhouse effect" can quickly raise the inside temperature to a lethal level.

Paper lunch bags are another useful type of container, particularly if you are collecting in the early morning, near lights, in search of moths for egg laying. Many such moths will begin laying eggs on the inside of the bag as soon as it is placed in the dark, and no additional accommodations may be necessary.

It is a matter of convenience whether you prefer to use belt pouches, fanny-pack, knapsack, or shoulder bag for carrying these assorted odds and ends. Your choice will be aided by several considerations, however. If you plan to photograph, keeping the camera instantly accessible and not in competition with carrying equipment is the first priority. Whatever the carrier, it is handy if its contents can be located by touch alone. Many times, if you take your eyes off a butterfly for even a second, you never see it again. Also, the carrier should not be such that it can shift position suddenly when you bend over, frightening your subject or upsetting your balance. The contents of the pack should be arranged so that they do not jostle about excessively. For these reasons we prefer belt pouches or fannypacks.

With the ability to transport live specimens safely, which in particular means protecting them from overstimulation, overheating, drying, and crushing, goes the responsibility of caring for them back at home. Any food plant not available close to home must be brought back in sufficient quantity to last, with refrigeration, until you can replenish the supply. The successful rearing of immature stages is the activity we find most fascinating. It is the subject of chapter 30.

CHAPTER
27

Baiting

While the most productive lep-watching is done where the moths and butterflies choose to be, there are times when attracting the insects to a place of your choice may be very useful. You may wish to persuade fast- or high-flying species to settle down where you can photograph them, or to discover what moths are actually out there in the dark, beyond the reach of our limited senses.

Having noticed that moths and butterflies are attracted to sap flows, rotting fruit, and carrion, lepidopterists long ago began furnishing these or substitute attractants where nature had failed to provide. Tapping a sugar maple in early spring can attract hundreds of cuculline moths to the sap flow at dusk. Concocting a substitute sweet, preferably a bit fermented, and painting it onto tree trunks can attract butterflies by day and underwing and other moths by night. Leaving chunks of rotting banana, apple, or other fruit in convenient places can concentrate fast-moving anglewings and admirals. A dead fish left on a beach soon becomes clothed with yellow tiger swallowtails. Juices dripped from a grill into the ashes of a campfire make the spot worth revisiting over the following few days.

Recipes for moth bait are many and varied but are basically solutions of sugar (hence the expression "sugaring" for moths) flavored with beer, molasses, or fruit. They are made more aromatic by fermentation, either natural or assisted by the addition of a bit of yeast. Some feel that the addition of stale urine improves the brew. The bait can be made up a batch at a time, or you may prefer to keep a "continuous soup" going, adding spoiled fruit, stale beer, wine dregs, molasses, brown sugar, or even dark rum or any fragrant wine, as these ingredients become available from time to time. A thick or syrupy mixture evaporates less rapidly than a thin one, but both are equally attractive. Bananas cut into one-inch chunks with the skin left on and steeped in the "soup" for a few days make very good lumps of bait. They can stand many hours of sunshine without drying out.

There are a few cautions with regard to bait. A pot of the brew can be a very "active" mixture, which may not tolerate being in a tightly closed jar because of generation of carbon dioxide. Explosion of a jar of sticky bait on the back seat of a car, or anywhere else, can be most distressing, and dangerous because of flying glass shards. At the same time, the pot should be kept carefully covered to exclude fruit flies, which will show up in droves if the bait has what it takes. We find that a weighted dish or saucer excludes the flies but allows venting. Tape can be used to hold the dish in place while traveling.

Bait can be used in a number of ways. Sugaring for moths is usually done by applying the bait to tree trunks with a paint brush, putting patches perhaps the size of your hand on areas of trunk not obstructed by projecting snags or adjacent shrubbery. This is best done just at dusk, when the hornets have retired for the night and the moths are becoming active. If you pick a route along the edge of a wood or along a woodland road, with reasonable footing, where you can make a round trip about every half hour, the results can be very rewarding.

Use of a battery-powered head lamp when making the rounds of the baited trees is helpful and leaves both hands free for other activities. Lacking that, an ordinary flashlight, wrapped with tape if necessary to keep it from being slippery, can be held snugly in one armpit. Moths can easily be "spooked" by too bright a light, yet one needs enough light to be able to focus a camera for flash photography. Taping a couple of layers of yellow paper napkin over the flashlight lens is a workable solution. If you wish to collect specimens of moths that are feeding at the bait, a net is of limited usefulness, since the moths will buzz madly about in the net and become damaged. Holding an open jar just beneath the feeding moth and nudging it with the rim will usually make the moth fly down into the jar, which you can then quickly cap. Females captured in this way are good sources of eggs, since they will already have mated and are now feeding up for their evening egg-laying activities.

Moth bait will attract more than moths. If you sugar a dead tree infested with carpenter ants, you may attract more ants than you ever needed to see, and their activity will usually discourage moths from settling down to feed. Beetles and centipedes seem less disruptive. The

Figure 27–1 Once-married underwing (*Catocala unijuga*) at bait, with sow bugs and slug

sight of a few glistening slugs gliding among feeding underwing moths is an impressive study in contrasts (fig. 27–1). And when a flying squirrel silently and suddenly alights on the collector instead of the tree, the effect has been understated to be startling. Whether these animals are more interested in the bait or in the bugs is uncertain, but it is probably a bit of both. (If you should have the opportunity to make a pet of a flying squirrel you should probably resist it. In New England, their fleas have recently been demonstrated to transmit the disease typhus to humans.)

When you are choosing a site for sugaring it is important to pick one that is appropriate, not just in the sense of its being a suitable habitat for moths, but in terms of permission from the owner. Be certain in advance that he knows what you wish to do and agrees to your being there. Landowners seeing lights moving slowly through their woodlots at night have been known to investigate with showers of shotgun pellets. And last but not least, cast a glance at the ground now and then. Skunks do not respond graciously to being jostled!

If you want to study the moths or butterflies in a particular area over an extended period and do not have the time to run a sugaring route night after night or watch bait stations in the daytime, the use of bait traps is helpful. A commonly used trap consists of a mesh cylinder with a closed top and an open bottom fitted with a net cone with the apex cut off. A bait container beneath the cone attracts the insects, which, after feeding, fly up into the cone and thence into the cylinder. As originally designed by Charles Rummel in the 1930s, the cylinder and cone were made of wire window screen, the top was closed with a cake pan or similar lid, and the trap was set on

1″ wooden blocks on a wooden platform on top of a post. The bait was placed in a small dish in the center of the platform. This type of trap had the disadvantage of being a more or less permanent setup, and removal of the lid to recover the insects often allowed some of the catch to escape. A more recent modification, by Dr. Austin Platt of the University of Maryland, makes the cylinder, cone, and top of nylon mesh, with a bait cup supported in a wire ring beneath the cone. The trap is suspended from a tree branch instead of being set on a post. It is collapsible and can be easily moved from place to place or packed for traveling. Figure 27–2 shows such a trap in use.

Figure 27–2 Collapsible bait trap in use

You can remove insects from the trap by reaching in through the cone with a small jar and maneuvering the bug into it. Some people modify the trap by sewing a zipper into the side of the cylinder.

As is the case with sugaring on tree trunks, the bait sometimes attracts creatures other than lepidoptera to the trap. White-faced and other hornets are particularly unwelcome. Those that you find in the bait cup when you are tending the trap may have just arrived and can be quite aggressive. On the other hand, those that have fed at the bait for a while or that have gone up into the trap seem to become quite mellow and are not particularly hazardous to work around (alcohol has its points). They do, however, have other unattractive habits. After sobering up, they may decide to make a meal off the lepidoptera in the trap, leaving it littered with detached moth and butterfly wings. One must philosophically accept the fact that the hornets are out to make a living and, for them, anything is fair game.

Another varmint for which it is sometimes hard to have charitable feelings is the raccoon. We try to hang our traps from thin branches, well away from tree trunks, and four to five feet from the ground (as high as possible and still be able to reach up to the top of the trap), but periodically one will be pulled down and ripped open, apparently, to judge by the tooth marks on the plastic bait cup, by a raccoon that leaped on it to eat the bait.

Rain also is a minor enemy, diluting the bait and reducing its effectiveness. A transparent plastic bag placed over the top of the trap makes a useful umbrella.

CHAPTER
28

Lights

The spectacle of the moth being attracted to the candle flame has been noted in literature for centuries, and lepidopterists have long taken advantage of this in their study of moths. Before Thomas Edison's time, collecting was done with the aid of lanterns. Before the advent of window screens, any room was a moth trap. As the use of outdoor electric lighting developed, a great deal of collecting was, and still is, done by examining light poles and the outsides of buildings for resting moths, either at night or in the early morning before the birds have helped themselves.

All types of lights are not equally attractive to moths. While they will indeed come to a candle or to a kerosene lantern, these light sources are yellowish, relatively weak, and not very effective. Ordinary incandescent light bulbs, with their broad spectrum of wavelengths, do quite well, and fluorescent tube lights of the whiter sorts are somewhat better. The most useful of the fluorescents is the "BL" or black light, with a moderate amount of bluish white visible light and a good output of near ultraviolet, which is particularly attractive to many species of moths. Red or orange insects viewed in this light reflect no red and appear gray or black, since the light source emits nothing at the red end of the spectrum. The "BLB" black-light tubes, of

the sort used to demonstrate fluorescence in minerals, attract quite effectively, but they are less easy to use because their only visible output is a bit of dark purple. They also have more of the shorter ultraviolet that can cause eye injury.

One further type of useful light is the mercury vapor bulb, which has a good output of the most attractive near ultraviolet wavelengths. These lights are so effective, however, that they have great drawing power. When they are used for outdoor lighting, as is a common practice along streets and near parking lots, immense numbers of moths can be attracted, often to their deaths. Travelers have told us of having visited gas stations where so many imperial and royal walnut moths were crushed on the pavement that the footing was unsafe. Fortunately the less expensive and more efficient sodium lights, which have very little attraction for moths, are beginning to replace the mercury vapor bulbs.

Both the fluorescent and the mercury vapor lights require special circuitry and ballasts, which increase their cost and somewhat limit flexibility of usage. However, the fluorescent lights can be wired to operate from a portable 12-volt battery, since they draw very little current. Use of a mercury vapor light in a remote field situation calls for a portable generator. Some types of mercury vapor bulb do not emit light of the most useful wavelengths and so attract poorly, but the GE H175A 39−22, or its equivalent, is very effective, with its major output at 365 nanometers. Another problem is the use of plastic sheathing to protect a fluorescent tube from breakage. Some plastics efficiently block the passage of the most desired ultraviolet wavelengths. It is a good idea to avoid staring at either a black light or a mercury vapor bulb, in order to avoid eye injury.

Using only lights that have been put up for the convenience of people limits the places that can be investigated. As in the case of baits, it is useful to take the light to a selected habitat, be it meadow,

Figure 28−1 Use of portable black light and sheet for collecting moths at night; portable battery case at lower right

woodland, swamp, or bog, to sample the species in those areas. A Coleman lantern is quite effective and can be taken anywhere. Most useful is a portable black light setup, although the necessary batteries may be quite heavy.

A portable light, rigged up almost anywhere so that it can shine across an open space, will attract moths, but it is most convenient to use it in connection with a sheet or a trap.

A white bed sheet is an invaluable piece of equipment. It gives good footing for the moths and good contrast for selecting desired specimens. It is lightweight and easy to transport. The black light should be suspended or propped so that it illuminates the sheet from a distance of about a foot. Attracted moths will circle about for a bit and eventually settle down to rest on the sheet. The sheet can be fixed to a wall with glass pushpins, or suspended from a line between two trees, using spring-clip clothespins. A length of sash cord makes the best line. The clothespins grip it well, and the knots are easy to untie. Wind is an element to be coped with: it is important to select a sheltered spot and to anchor the lower end of the sheet with some rocks or logs to keep it from flapping about (fig. 28–1). A good approach, when you can drive into the collecting spot, is to hang the sheet on the car. Cabinet-door magnets are used to hold the top edge of the sheet onto the roof. The black light can be suspended from a stick equipped with two similar magnets and laid on the roof, or from a small branch closed into the top edge of a door so that it projects about a foot. If you collect in a place where there are no trees between which to hang a line, as in a bog or prairie, you can lay the sheet on the ground and prop up the black light in the center with the help of an inverted

Y-shaped stick. The drawback of this is that you have to collect on your hands and knees, rather than upright.

Much has been written about the best kinds of nights for collecting moths, and there is no question that weather, barometric conditions, and the phase of the moon are significant. When Alfred Russell Wallace was making his journey through the Malay Archipelago in 1860, he remained in one village for about two months while convalescing from an illness. Night after night he observed and recorded the amount of moth activity around a lantern on his veranda. He concluded that clear nights were least productive, especially if the moon was bright. Overcast, still nights were excellent. A light rain or drizzle improved the situation even more, but a heavy downpour was deleterious. He did not observe whether the moths refrained from flying in heavy rain, or whether they were dashed to the ground and incapacitated. In general, the observations are similar in temperate climates. If the night is clear, the barometer is rising, and a cold front has just passed through, even without a significant drop in temperature, collecting is likely to be poor. Some of our best collecting nights have been spent beneath umbrellas or ponchos in a developing drizzle. It is then that the practice of hanging the sheet from the side of the car becomes particularly attractive, and the car can also be a handy refuge from insistent mosquitos.

Now is perhaps the time to emphasize that, while we hope and believe that the suggestions and comments offered in this book are valid and helpful, anyone who takes them as "gospel" or "the last word" will undoubtedly be missing big opportunities. A friend once told us that he set up his black light beneath a full moon on a Central American hilltop and was bombarded by sphinx moths. The essence of lep-watching, or anything scientific, is experimentation and innovation. Try anything that you think might be interesting or productive. What we have found unrewarding in one area may turn out to be just right somewhere else.

Time of night also has a bearing on collecting. Many species of moths are active during only a few hours each night, some early after dark, some in the middle of the night, some just before dawn. This seems to be related to the timing of their mating activities, which may take place at different times of the night to reduce competition among related species. When we are spending several days in an area with good moth collecting and do not wish to stay up all night every night, we will often collect for just a few hours, but at different times, each night. This was particularly beneficial one night in Ecuador when, while it was still totally dark between 5 and 6 A.M., the black light attracted crepuscular skipper butterflies that were not seen at any other time.

There are situations when it is desirable to be able to collect moths all night long, for a number of nights or throughout a season, without the fatigue of staying up all night. A light trap provides the solution. While we have built traps of many different designs, using either black light or a mercury vapor bulb, the Robinson trap or an adaptation of it is one of the best. As we build ours, it consists of a galvanized steel wash tub about 21″ in diameter with numerous drain holes drilled in the center of the bottom. A 1″-high plastic rim, cemented to the bottom with silicone caulking compound, keeps rainwater from spreading over the bottom of the tub. A low conical cover is made from flexible polycarbonate plastic about 2 mm thick, with the top cut out to make an opening about 8″ in diameter. Into this opening is cemented a plastic funnel with the bottom cut off to leave an opening about 2″ in diameter. Beneath this opening is placed an open 2½″ plastic cylinder (cut from an 8-ounce plastic bottle), held on with fiberglass-reinforced strapping tape. A mercury

Figure 28–2 Tub trap with mercury vapor light

vapor bulb, base up, is held in place immediately above the center of the funnel by a frame of three plexiglass fins, and the bulb and socket are shielded from rain by a plexiglass disk on top (figs. 28–2, 28–3, and 28–4). While the original Robinson trap design, with the bulb base down and no protection from the elements, may be a little more efficient in

catching moths, we prefer not to have the expensive mercury vapor bulbs shattered by hail or sudden downpours.

In order to provide roosting places for the trapped moths, so that they will not spend the night buzzing futilely about, the inside of the tub should be stacked with inverted cardboard egg boxes (bottom halves). Some species of moths

Figure 28–3 Tub trap opened to show cover, light fixture, and arrangement of egg cartons

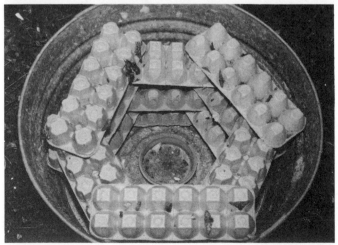

Figure 28–4 Bottom of tub trap, showing drain details

prefer to rest on the brightly lighted upper surfaces, and some crawl into the shaded areas underneath.

On visiting the trap in the morning, which should be done before the sun can heat up the tub and agitate or even kill the inhabitants, you should first inspect the grass and weeds within a few yards of the trap. Here may be roosting a great variety of moths of all sizes, in natural resting positions, ideal subjects for photography. In view of the fact that moths normally rest in the daytime in places where you will have trouble finding them, and may disturb them into flight if you do, the area outside the trap presents an opportunity not to be missed. The resting postures of moths present many surprises and striking camouflages, which in themselves are worthy of more study and record than they have received. But be there early, before the birds have made their rounds. Fast film or fill flash may be necessary for good photographs, although we avoid flash whenever possible in order to have more natural backgrounds.

When the trap is opened, a few moths will usually be disturbed and will rapidly depart. But the majority, if the temperature has not risen yet, will remain at rest. You can gently pick up one egg box at a time, look over its resting customers, and knock the individuals you wish to retain into jars or small paper bags, just one to a container if you are saving the specimens alive. Putting more than one into a container leads to damage from repeated flight. Unwanted moths are merely knocked off the boxes and allowed to escape. While ideally one should empty the trap in a different place every day to outwit the birds and reduce predation of released moths, birds are not that easily fooled. Within a few days of setting up a trap, we find a resident catbird or bluejay following us every morning to help check it, regardless of how we may move the trap.

CHAPTER

29

Lures and Other Collecting Methods

Over the past two hundred years amateur lepidopterists have devised a number of collecting methods other than net, bait, and light. While they are useful only in special situations, they are interesting as well as productive.

There are times when a bit of color can be used as a lure for male butterflies. Our first experience with this was in Alaska, where we noted that a yellow rain jacket, thrown on the tundra when the sun came out, was promptly but briefly investigated by a number of male lesser fritillaries (genus *Boloria*). The attraction was most certainly the color, rather than any contained perspiration, since a dark-green rain jacket, which unquestionably was better supplied with perspiration, received no such attention. A friend whose special interest is in the larger fritillaries (genus *Speyeria*) tells us that he has often used an orange as a lure: he lobs the orange into the air, then claps his net over it as it strikes the ground. In so doing he will sometimes capture a male fritillary that is challenging the presence of this strange orange flying object in his territory. In Florida, we have used orange-and-white fishing floats, tossed into the air alongside a fig tree, to lure male ruddy daggerwings (*Marpesia petreus*) within reach of a net.

If you are ever in the habitat of the *Morpho* butterflies, those incomparably brilliant, large, blue butterflies of tropical America, a piece of cobalt-blue cloth the size of a playing card, attached to your hat, will often attract a territorial male *Morpho* within easy viewing distance, or in some instances too close to photograph. If the lure works, and there are any net-swinging lepidopterists in your vicinity, it is better to take hat in hand to avoid risk of decapitation. The sight of a *Morpho* can whip the most conservative lepidopterist into a heedless frenzy.

As the range of the gypsy moth continues to extend, we have become familiar with the use of a chemical lure, the pheromone emitted by the female gypsy moth, to attract and trap males. This chemical, which is essential to the mating activities of the gypsies, is of relatively little interest to lep-watchers, since we rarely need help in watching gypsy moths. The bobbing, erratic flight of the males is so distracting that we need instead to learn to ignore them in favor of more interesting subjects.

Pheromones for other species are of greater interest, however, particularly those of the clearwing borer moths. The larvae of this group of moths feed within the stems or trunks of various soft or woody plants, often causing significant commercial damage, as in the case of squash vines or peach trees. Commercially available pheromones will attract the adult males of these species, but also the males of many other species that otherwise may be extremely difficult to find. Observations with the use of these chemicals can uncover new information on their spectrum of attractiveness, and on the numbers of species occurring in a particular area. New chemicals are being synthesized each year, and as they become available they will broaden the horizons of the lep-watcher.

At times while out collecting, you may be startled by the very persistent presence of a "wasp," hovering about the front of your shirt. When you finally recall that you have a sample of pheromone clipped to your shirt pocket, the threatening intruder becomes a welcome visitor, a clearwing moth. If you wish to know which species he is, he will have to be captured, since many of the species are so closely similar that field identification is unreliable.

From time to time lep-watchers have been pleased to discover that various colognes and after-shave lotions are very successful in seducing clearwing moths. These scents are apparently less successful in their intended task, since they tend not to remain long on the market. But other brands always come along!

Adult underwing moths usually rest during the day in spots where they can be sheltered or camouflaged. They can be found on the sides of buildings, behind shutters, under eaves, beneath bridges. If their choice is the bark of a tree, they may be virtually invisible. It is here that an implement designed for hitting flies—a baseball bat—becomes useful. If you will explore the woods on a hot day in mid or late summer and give small to medium-size trees a hefty whack with the bat, you will often jar a resting underwing into flight. With luck, you can then follow it to its next landing place.

Beating the bushes—tapping end or top branches of shrubs and small trees with your net handle—will frequently set a perching hairstreak into flight. Because they are territorial, they usually return to the same spot, at which point observation becomes easy.

Beating for larvae is another productive activity. If you invert an open umbrella beneath a branch and strike the branch sharply with a stick, feeding larvae will lose their footholds and fall into the umbrella. The blow must be bold and assertive. A tentative tap will alert the caterpillars to hold on, and you will accomplish little. It is a good idea to beat branches of just one species of tree at a time, so there will be no confusion as to the food plant from which the larva was dislodged. While you may succeed in carrying several species of larvae home in one container, each species should be reared separately, or you may end up with one fat noctuid and a number of assorted corpses.

If you can develop an eye for feeding damage, your search for larvae will be more productive. Growing tips that lack small leaves often point to a larva resting farther down the stem, but if a considerable portion of the branch tip itself is missing, suspect a browsing deer. A milkweed leaf with the midrib cut and oozing indicates a monarch caterpillar nearby. Leaves with pieces missing from the edge have frequently been damaged by caterpillars, but holes punched out of leaves are more often the work of beetles. A freshly cut edge suggests that the caterpillar might still be in the vicinity, while a browned edge indicates that the diner is long gone. Many microlepidoptera larvae make mines and galleries by feeding between the two layers of the leaf; they show as translucent paths and patches. And often very young larvae, or the larvae of lycaenids, will scrape cells only from the undersurface of the leaf, leaving translucent windows.

Frass is a valuable clue to the presence of caterpillars. Any patch of bare ground should be inspected for the little cylindrical black pellets, often sculptured like hand grenades. Their presence is good evidence of a larva overhead, although in a dry season the frass can persist for many days without deteriorating. The caterpillar may have moved on to greener pastures or may already have pupated.

Signs of borer activity are quite different. Wilted or withered stems direct your attention to the healthy part of the stem below, where the borer is hidden. Often a pile of moist, matted frass will be found extruding from a hole in the side of the stem. Dealing with borers presents several challenges that are discussed in chapter 30, on rearing.

Larvae that migrate down tree trunks in the daytime can often be intercepted by tying a tangle of burlap or newspaper, with plenty of folds and wrinkles, around the lower part of the trunk. Descending larvae will rest there and can readily be found during the day. Many times they end up pupating in these artificial shelters.

In the midnineteenth century in England, the Reverend Joseph Greene published a little pamphlet on the subject of pupa digging. He recommended removing, with an ordinary trowel, a block of sod 6″–8″ broad and a few inches deep from angles between roots at the base of the tree. This area, where it was uncovered, was then to be inspected for cocoons and pupae, and the sod shaken apart to look for buried pupae. Finally, a search was to be made beneath any flakes of bark on the lower part of the trunk, and within any adhering clumps of moss. The best yield was from large trees isolated in meadows or pastures, and the best season from late summer to early winter. He found the rewards meager in woods and forests. We have had little experience with this method of collecting, largely because appropriate terrain is scarce in our part of New England. However, where likely situations exist, the procedure should be worth trying.

Rearing Immature Stages

There are few lep-watchers who, upon discovering an interesting caterpillar in the field, can resist the urge to take it home, feed it in captivity, and discover what it will turn into. Since most of the field guides illustrate only a few types of larvae, many of your finds will be intriguing mysteries. With a few tips as to how to rear larvae successfully, you can rapidly become an accomplished detective.

As described already in chapter 26, one of the most important steps is bringing your new acquaintance home safely,

Figure 30–1 Rearing containers (*clockwise from upper left*): half-gallon ice cream box; gallon glass jar; honeycomb box; small plastic box

along with a supply of food plant protected against wilting en route. Carrying the food in a sealed plastic bag with a little added moisture and transporting the caterpillar in a vial or box with one or two leaves work very well. Carrying the caterpillar in the wet bag can lead to death by drowning. Once at home, there are several useful ways to house the critter.

Transparent plastic boxes, such as square honeycomb boxes, are very handy. The box will need a layer of moist paper towel on the bottom, and a few leaves of food plant. Replace the lid tightly, so that neither the moisture nor the caterpillar can escape. There will be enough oxygen in the container to allow the caterpillar to thrive between daily openings to clean out droppings and replenish food. Any transparent plastic box with a snugly fitting cover works well. Covered glass jars are equally useful, but in some respects less convenient in shape, especially if you wish to photograph the larva without disturbing it. A very convenient container can be made from a bowl-shaped half-gallon plastic ice cream box. Cut a large circular piece out of the center of the lid, sparing the outer half inch, lay a sheet of transparent plastic wrap over the box, and replace the lid. The plastic film allows you to see what is going on without having to open the box (fig. 30–1). Daily cleaning of the

149

boxes is important to avoid mold growth on frass and wilted foliage. Failure to do this can result in high mortality. Boxes should be thoroughly washed with detergent and water and allowed to dry before being reused, to reduce possible transmission of disease.

Closed containers should not be put in the sun. They can easily overheat and cook their inhabitants.

Another good approach is to place stems of the food plant in water in a narrow-necked bottle to keep them fresh. Any remaining space in the neck of the bottle should be plugged with paper towel to prevent the caterpillar from climbing down the stems into the water. The bottle should then be placed in a screened cage with the caterpillar on the food plant (fig. 30–2). Alternatively a mesh bag can be placed over the food plant and the open end tied snugly with a string about the neck of the bottle, or about the plant stems. It is helpful to suspend the top of the bag with a string from above, to keep the bottle from blowing over in a breeze (fig. 30–3). The bottle method has the advantage that the

Figure 30–2 Screen rearing cage, using pizza pans for top and bottom

Figure 30–3 Rearing larvae in mesh bag indoors

Figure 30–4 Muslin sleeve for outdoor rearing

frass dries out instead of getting moldy, so daily changes are unnecessary. Sun is not dangerous, if there is enough foliage so that the caterpillar can always find a shady spot. Photographing can be done easily by removing the bottle from the cage or bag.

If you are faced with the prospect of rearing a large number of larvae of one species, such as a colony of mourning cloak or buck moth caterpillars, "bagging" or "sleeving" on growing trees or shrubs is ideal. Made of nylon mosquito netting or lightweight muslin, a sleeve is long and cylindrical and open at both ends, while bags have the proportions of a pillowcase and in addition to being open at one end, may have a small opening at the other end for introduction of caterpillars or removal of frass. These enclosures can be made any size you wish, depending on the size of the branch and the number of caterpillars you wish to enclose. For convenience, they should cover enough food to last a week or two.

When using a bag or sleeve, place it over the end of a branch and pull it down, without crumpling the foliage at the end. Tie the bottom end snugly about a bare place on the branch (figs. 30–4 and 30–5). There should be no openings through which caterpillars can escape. Then introduce the larvae

Figure 30–5 Nylon mesh bag for outdoor rearing

through the other end, and close the opening with string. It is a good idea to try to place the larvae directly onto the leaves or twigs, especially if they are very young. Otherwise they may wear themselves out wandering over the inner surface of the bag in search of something to eat.

If you are using a bag with only one opening, the larvae must obviously be introduced before the bag is tied about the branch. Bending the branch downward reduces the likelihood of the caterpillars falling out during the loading process.

Before placing a bag on a branch, it is wise to look the branch over carefully for predators, particularly spiders and stinkbugs. One such uninvited guest will fatten up happily (if such emotion is within its ken) on your choicest larvae and leave you with an empty bag.

One bonus from bagging is finding within the bag other species already on the branch as eggs or larvae too small to be noticed. In the shelter of the bag, they thrive and become more mysteries to be solved. The same thing can happen when you are gathering food for indoor rearing. On one occasion we started off with a single black swallowtail caterpillar, but the wild carrot leaves we picked for it carried so many hidden eggs we ended rearing more than a dozen!

If you are rearing a caterpillar indoors you may notice that for a period of a day or half a day it consumes no food, produces no frass, and remains motionless, sometimes on the side of the box instead of on the food plant. If you are unlucky this may signal the impending emergence of some internal parasitoids, or the onset of some viral or bacterial disease. In the normal course of events, however, this is merely the resting phase at the end of the instar, just before the larva

sheds its old head capsule and skin. If it is necessary to clean the box at this time, it is best to try to clean around the caterpillar and leave it undisturbed. It will usually be resting on a thin pad of silk in which the legs of the old skin are anchored. Removing it from this pad may make it difficult for the caterpillar to climb out of its old skin. A larva ready to moult is easily recognized: the head capsule seems cocked forward and a new and larger one is dimly visible behind it. By the next day, after having moulted, it will again become active and resume eating.

There are times when you will come across a caterpillar in the field, crawling rather rapidly and in a very determined manner across an open area, giving no clue as to what its food plant may be. If the caterpillar is relatively large, you may not need to know. It may already have finished feeding and be wandering in search of a place to pupate.

When a caterpillar has finished eating and begins to wander, it has special needs for pupation. In the case of most butterflies, whose larvae wish to suspend themselves beneath some sheltered horizontal or oblique surface, the rearing container itself will provide a satisfactory spot. But from the lep-watcher's point of view, this is not ideal: photographing a chrysalis, or the butterfly emerging from it, on the underside of a cage lid is not very attractive. A few dead twigs or sticks, placed leaning within the rearing cage, will often induce the larva to suspend in a more natural-appearing situation and form its chrysalis there.

Larvae of the lycaenids (coppers, blues, and hairstreaks), which form their chrysalids among leaf litter on or near the ground, should be supplied with some crumpled dried leaves at pupation time. Once the pupae are formed, you may have a bit of a treasure hunt trying to locate them where they are skillfully concealed within curled leaf edges, or, as we found on one memorable occasion, within an empty acorn cup!

Moth larvae that spin cocoons usually take care of themselves among the twigs and leaves within the rearing container or bag. Luna, polyphemus, and io often pull together folds of the bag itself instead of using leaves. When the cocoon has matured for a week or so the surrounding cloth or netting can be peeled off safely.

If you are rearing moth larvae that normally wander off after feeding to pupate in leaf litter or beneath the soil, they can be transferred, as soon as wandering begins, to a bucket or wooden box two thirds filled with loose soil, humus gleaned from the forest floor, or peat or sphagnum moss. The latter have the advantage of being clean and easy to handle. The larvae will burrow just beneath the surface, or deeply, according to their preferences, and hollow out cells in which to pupate. Larger larvae, such as sphinxes or the imperial moth, should be left at least a week or ten days undisturbed, since they may have a very long prepupal stage once they have built their cells.

Prepupal larvae of ground-pupating species, reared in bags or sleeves, will suffer from drying and excessive heat if they cannot be removed from the bag within a few hours after feeding is completed. When such larvae are nearly grown, it is therefore a good idea to put a large mass of damp sphagnum moss or leaf litter in the bottom of the bag to provide shelter between your visits to remove them.

A few species of agaristine moths, such as the eight-spotted forester and the pearly wood nymph, have larvae that burrow into dead wood to pupate. A handful of dead sticks of pine or other soft wood placed in the rearing container will simplify their efforts. Such species should not be reared in containers covered with plastic film or made of wood. The larvae will chew their way out, or burrow into the cage wall to pupate!

Borers present a special challenge. Caterpillars that feed within the stems of plants are themselves invisible, but most of them leave a hole in the stem through which they eject their droppings. The frass usually accumulates about the hole and may be looked for specifically if you know the food plant of a particular species. Or the infested plant may be located by looking for stalks with wilted or withered tops. Squash borers may be found in this way, as can the fully grown larvae of the giant skipper, *Megathymus yuccae*.

Once the borer has been located, the question becomes how to rear it. If discovered in late winter or early spring, the giant skipper larva will have finished feeding. The stalk containing the burrow can be cut off, and the bottom end plugged with a wad of paper. The larva tends to stay at the top of its burrow. Pupation and emergence are then awaited; the butterfly escapes through a woven chimney at the top of the stalk. For the larvae of *Papaipema* (very colorful noctuid moths that emerge in the autumn), the whole plant can often be dug and maintained in healthy condition until the larva has pupated in the adjacent soil. Another approach is to leave the plant alone until pupation has occurred, then search through the upper layers of soil within a radius of one to two feet to find the pupa. In soft plants, such as squash vines, one can only keep segments of stem in humid containers and let the larva transfer from one to another. Whatever the approach, it is important to prevent drying of the stem, since this may cause it to shrink and trap or crush the larva or pupa within.

Dealing with diapause is one of the most important, and occasionally difficult, steps in rearing lepidoptera. In temperate or colder climates, species that overwinter in the egg need merely to have the eggs stored in a place where the temperature will be near to or below freezing for at least a few weeks during the winter. They should be in containers that limit drying but will not have enough moisture to allow mold growth. Pill vials, placed in an unheated garage or cellar entry, protected from large fluctuations of temperature, can serve very well for the eggs of hairstreaks, underwings, and the like. In the spring, the vials must be checked at least daily for hatching; the tiny larvae will dry out and die if not transferred promptly to their proper food plant. Ideally the vials should be allowed to warm up just at the time that the food plant leaf buds are bursting open, so a supply of fresh, tender young leaflets will be available to the hatching caterpillars.

In the event that eggs hatch prematurely, as a result of poor timing on your part or on the part of the caterpillars, a zealot of our acquaintance has come up with a maneuver that can help. One January he received through the mail some eggs that, because of exposure to the warmth of the post office, had hatched by the time he opened the package. Not wanting to lose the batch, he took winter buds from an oak tree, peeled off the bud scales, and allowed the larvae to feed on the partly formed leaves within. By the time the dozen or so larvae reached maturity a month later, the number of leaf buds he had peeled was astronomical!

Care of pupae through the winter is likewise straightforward. They need the same chilling as do eggs but need more attention to humidity. Underground pupae survive well in a box of damp peat moss, which should be sprayed with water periodically during the winter to prevent drying out. Mice can be kept out with wire screening. In the spring the box can be transferred to a cage or a screened porch, where each species will emerge at its proper season.

Emergence cages are a necessity, so that newly hatched moths and butterflies can find good footing and space to expand their wings. Small, individual cages are particularly important, so that pupae of unknown larvae can be kept carefully segregated and labeled. An excellent small cage is made from a cat-food can with a few nail holes in the bottom (punched from the inside out) for drainage. A vertical cylinder of window-screen wire (joined with hot-melt glue) is capped with a transparent plastic lid. The bottom of a petrie dish is just the right size. Larger cages of the same sort can be made from metal cake boxes (fig. 30–6). A layer of moistened peat or sphagnum provides protection for the pupa.

When the hibernating stage is the larva, as is the case with many of the nymphalid and satyrid butterflies, tiger moths, and geometrid moths, the problems vary from simple to very difficult. In general, there should be enough humidity to prevent dehydration of the larvae, yet not so much as to favor mold growth. Large temperature fluctuations need to be avoided; the temperature should ideally hover a few degrees above freezing. Recognizing when diapause is beginning is important, since larva should not be thrust into a cold environment while they are still feeding actively, nor should they be allowed to remain warm long after feeding has stopped. For this reason, species that are going to hibernate as larvae may best be reared out of doors in the fall, where they can respond to the gradual shortening of daylight hours and to the gradual drop in average temperatures.

There are numerous approaches. We have had good success with geometrids by simply leaving them all winter in a cold garage away from sunlight, perching on twigs of food plant in closed glass jars. Some people have success by putting arctiids into glass jars loosely filled with dead leaves and closed with a piece of heavy cloth tied over the top. The jars (inverted to prevent accumulation of water) are then placed on the ground on the north side of a building and covered with a large pile of dead leaves until spring. Others enclose the larvae with a few food plant leaves in tightly closed containers, wrap all the containers in a plastic garbage bag, and bury it underground in a shaded area.

A refrigerator can be used for hibernation. In this case the containers should be clean, free of any frass or bits of vegetation, and fitted with some slightly damp paper towels. They should be left in a cool, dark place for a number of days until the larvae cease wandering, and then should be placed in a refrigerator at 38°–40°F. with the containers tightly closed.

When the larvae are brought out of storage in the spring and are furnished with food, some begin to feed promptly, while some may delay several days before showing any appetite.

Those species of noctuid larvae that go into summer diapause or aestivation also

Figure 30–6 Emergence cages made from cake boxes and cat-food can

require special handling. They eat ravenously while the leaves are still tender in the spring and early summer but for some reason choose to wait until late summer or fall to pupate. In the wild, they would seek shelter and protection from drying and overheating by hiding beneath the leaf litter or in the upper layers of the soil. When reared in captivity, they survive well in a box partly filled with damp peat moss into which they can burrow. The box should be kept in a cool cellar and the peat dampened periodically.

Species that feed up early, promptly pupate, and await the cooler weather of the fall for emergence can be carried through the summer in the same fashion, with the pupae buried in damp peat.

Rearing caterpillars found by chance is very satisfying, but seeking out eggs, larvae, and pupae to rear can be even more so. Sometimes you may wish to rear a number of one species to observe variations in coloring or behavior, to use in classrooms, or to obtain a number of perfect adult specimens for a collection. Whatever the reason, the question is how to obtain numerous eggs or larvae of a particular species.

In the case of moths, obtaining eggs can be extremely easy. A wild female of a large silk moth such as luna, polyphemus, cecropia, or their relatives, if captured when attracted to artificial light, will almost certainly have mated, since females of these species usually mate before they start to fly about. If you enclose such a moth in a large paper bag with the top folded shut, she will usually spend the night laying eggs, often several hundred, gluing them to the inside of the bag. Since these saturniids have no digestive tracts as adults, they do not need to be fed. Anisotas and the imperial and royal walnut moths respond to the same treatment. Sphinx moths are equally accommodating, but they often wait several nights in the bag before they begin to lay. Because sphinxes can feed and need to feed, they may do better if you place in the bag a tightly rolled "cigar" of paper towel soaked in a solution of sugar or honey (a 20 percent concentration is satisfactory). Spraying the inside of the bag daily to keep up humidity can be helpful. A spray bottle such as is used for houseplants is handy for this. Occasionally a sphingid seems to produce better if there is a sprig of larval food plant in the bag, but this is usually not necessary, and it is difficult to keep the foliage from wilting.

Keep in mind that maturing larvae have prodigious appetites, which may strain your ability to keep them supplied with groceries! Therefore, once the moth has laid enough eggs for your purposes, she can be released. The eggs and the underlying paper to which they adhere should be cut from the bag with scissors and placed in a transparent plastic box. There they will be protected from ants and other predators and can be easily observed for hatching. With the saturniids and sphingids, this usually occurs in about ten to fourteen days.

Female underwing moths, captured occasionally at artificial light but far more commonly at bait, can also be induced to lay eggs in paper bags, but they appreciate more sophisticated accommodations. Their natural practice is to deposit eggs in crevices in the bark of the larval food tree. In captivity some species, particularly the small ones whose larvae feed on apple, hawthorne, and cherry, like to tuck their eggs into the seam of the paper bag and under the folds at the bottom, quite out of sight. Some will use chinks in chunks of bark from the food tree placed in the bag.

Many will hide their eggs in the folds of a tightly wadded paper towel or within the mesh of a strip of burlap wound tightly around a block of wood. A few ignore these accommodations and lay their eggs anywhere in the bag. While most species don't seem to require a piece of the food plant, those using sweetfern, gale, and bayberry often benefit from having a sprig of one of these aromatic plants included. With catocalas, feeding and humidity are essential. The "cigar" of sugar-soaked paper towel works well. As the water evaporates, it can be replenished by daily squirts of water from the spray bottle (focused for a narrow stream) at the same time you spray the inside of the bag. Replacing the "cigar" weekly, or as it develops mold, is beneficial, but unroll it and examine it carefully. The moth may have tucked eggs between the folds. We have had moths handled this way live and deposit fertile eggs over a period of four weeks.

The bags should be placed where they will be protected from excessive heat and direct sunlight and still have a normal number of hours of darkness.

After the eggs are harvested, they can be kept in plastic pill vials in the cold. When the eggs hatch in the spring, some species hatch all at once, and some are spread out over a period of several weeks.

Many of the smaller noctuids and geometrids will respond to the simple paper bag approach (fig. 30–7), with a source of sugar and water, or will perform in a glass jar containing a sugar source and a crumpled piece of paper. Excess moisture and enhanced mold growth can be problems with the use of jars.

If the guides and reference books do not indicate whether the eggs will hatch

Figure 30–7 Ova of hollow-spotted plagodis (*Plagodis alcoolaria*) laid on the edge of a paper bag

promptly, or after a period of diapause, it may be possible to guess what to expect by the season of the year that the moth was flying. If eggs are laid in spring and early summer, they usually hatch in about a week, whereas those laid in later summer and autumn commonly diapause through the winter. There are so many exceptions, however, that close watching is necessary for species with unfamiliar life histories, and you will probably "miss the boat" many times. Such is part of the adventure of rearing.

The tiger moths are probably the least inhibited egg layers. Often a female popped into a pill vial in the field will have laid dozens of eggs, loose and rolling about in the vial, by the time you reach home!

Butterflies are a different story. In order to inspire a captive female to lay eggs, you must provide not only food in the form of a wad of cotton or sponge soaked in sugar water and the proper larval food plant on which she can lay her eggs, but the right amount of warmth, light, and humidity. All this needs to be so arranged that her tendency to fly to the brightest part of her enclosure will bring her into close proximity, if not indeed actual contact, with her food and the larval food.

One setup that can accomplish this starts with an ordinary unglazed clay flowerpot (an item that is becoming increasingly hard to find), of a diameter at least three or four times the wingspan of the butterfly with which you are working. Dampen the pot thoroughly, and set the bottom into a tin can or jar of a size that will support the base of the pot a few inches above the bottom of the container; fill the can with enough water to touch the bottom of the pot. Put a few sprigs of the larval food plant, cut just long enough so that they will almost reach the top of the pot, through the hole in the bottom and into the water. Plug any remaining space in the hole with paper. Using a thread, suspend the wad of cotton just inside the top of the pot, and cover the pot with a square of glass or a clear plastic lid. Arrange a gooseneck lamp or similar fixture, with a 60–75-watt bulb, so that the pot can be illuminated from an adjustable distance from above.

You can now place the female in the pot, leaving the light off for a while so that she can become adjusted to her surroundings. Then illuminate the pot for periods of two hours at time, with intervals to rest in between, adjusting the height to keep the pot warm and bright, but not hot. Add water to the jar or can as necessary, to keep the base of the pot moist. Many butterflies handled in this way will lay dozens of eggs, while others, of the same or different species, may be totally unproductive.

A simpler approach, useful for species whose larvae feed on grass, such as skippers and satyrids, uses a large glass jar laid on its side. Grass is laid lengthwise on the bottom, the butterfly placed within, and the jar closed with some mesh fabric. Light is used as with the previous method. The butterfly should be given the opportunity to feed on sugar solution daily.

Some butterflies will also respond to bagging on a branch of the host plant out of doors. The bag should be of mesh rather than muslin, to allow for plenty of sunlight and ventilation. It should not be tightly packed with foliage, or there will be no place for the butterfly to flutter about. If the larval food plant does not have nectar-bearing blossoms for the butterfly, it helps to supply sugar water regularly on a piece of sponge. If finding the eggs proves to be too difficult, leave the branch bagged for a few weeks and then look for larval feeding damage.

You may at times wish to obtain eggs from insects that have emerged in captivity and have had no opportunity to mate in the wild. Saturniids mate readily in captivity in a moderately roomy cage or on a screened porch. A female can be "tied out" to attract and mate with a wild male. Make a cylinder of screen wire about 6" in diameter and 15" long, suspended horizontally by a wire coat hanger. Using soft, lightweight string, pass a noose gently but snugly about the thorax of the female, between the forewings and hind wings, then run the free end of the string through the center of the roof of the cylinder and secure it at the neck of the hanger. Leave a few inches of slack in the string so that the moth can walk about on the roof of the cage (fig. 30–8). If you than hang the cage on a sheltered branch at night (in the afternoon, in the case of the promethea moth), the female will start broadcasting her pheromone, attract wild males, and mate. When mating has been completed the following afternoon, the noose can be cut loose and the female placed in a paper bag for egg laying.

If your goal is to obtain matings between individuals you are rearing, and you do not have simultaneous emergences of opposite sexes, an early emergent can be stored for a number of days in an envelope at normal refrigerator temperatures until an insect of the opposite sex comes out.

Cold storage can also be used to delay emergence of pupae. If you wish to time emergence of saturniid cocoons to coincide with a summer camp program, for example, move the cocoons into a refrigerator in late winter and leave them

Figure 30–8 Mating cylinder for saturniid moths

there until a few weeks before the desired emergence time. Periodic sprinkling is most important; refrigerators dry cocoons out quickly.

Repeated inbreeding of successive generations of home-reared stock has its disadvantages. The moths become successively smaller and less prolific, and eventually they fail to mate. At the same time, recessive features occasionally become apparent. We inbred io moths for six generations and eventually males appeared with apricot-colored, rather than yellow, forewings, and solid black discal spots instead of vague, blackish rings. At that point we were unable to achieve further matings.

Rearing is a challenge, a pleasure, and a responsibility. The importance of preventing the release or escape of a species being reared where it is not native cannot be overemphasized.

31

Making a Permanent Collection

At various points earlier in the book, we have mentioned permanent preservation of specimens. This and the next chapter are devoted to various techniques for preparing specimens for permanent collections, and to the means of protecting the collections so that they will remain in good condition for hundreds of years, long after we as collectors are certainly gone and possibly forgotten (except for those little pin-labels memorializing our efforts!).

In order for a moth or butterfly to be saved permanently in proper condition for study or admiration it must be dead, spread, dried, and labeled. By "spread" we mean symmetrically arranged so that the wings are readily viewed, in a conventional position, with the antennae visible and as safe as possible from damage. The usual position is with the hind edges of the forewings forming a straight line, at right angles to the axis of the body, and the hind wings brought forward so that they are just slightly overlapped by the forewings; all four wings should lie in the same horizontal plane. A pin through the center of the thorax, perpendicular to the axis of the insect's body and to the plane of the wings, allows for safe handling of the specimen and provides a permanent place for the data label.

Drying, curiously enough, is all that it takes to preserve an adult insect permanently. The skeleton of an insect is on the outside and consists largely of cuticle that is quite rigid, except for a few areas such as the membranes between the segments of the abdomen. (Comparison with a tin can is rather extreme, but not entirely inappropriate.) As a result, when the interior soft parts of the body dry out, very little shrinkage occurs. It is also curious that, as this drying occurs, there is no spoiling or putrefaction, such as occurs with soft-bodied larvae or with fish, birds, and other animals. It appears to be a matter of spontaneous mummification. Once the interior of the body has become thoroughly dried—within a few days to a few weeks, depending on humidity and the size of the insect body— the wings and other body parts will remain permanently in the position in which they were held during the drying period.

KILLING INSECTS

The insect to be preserved must be dead, but clearly not dead of old age, because at that point it will be so worn and damaged as to be of little interest or value.

What, then, are appropriate ways to kill moths or butterflies without damaging their wings or scales? The approach one takes to a dining mosquito or an errant cockroach is clearly not the answer. We have already discussed bringing specimens back from the field in envelopes or vials. Placing these in a freezer for a few hours will quickly numb and kill the insects. They can then be taken out and allowed to warm to room temperature, for spreading or for transfer to labeled envelopes for more prolonged storage in closed plastic boxes in the freezer. It is important not to handle the specimens until they have thawed. They are exceedingly brittle when frozen hard. In fact, if you accidentally drop a vial from the freezer onto the floor, the contained butterfly may shatter like glass.

Some people develop the knack of pinching a butterfly to kill it—squeezing the sides of the thorax with the wings folded up over the back, pinching just hard enough between thumb and forefinger to kill the insect without mashing it. You must not allow this pressure to be applied to the abdomen, or its contents may be extruded and the specimen damaged. It is very difficult to apply this method safely to very delicate butterflies, such as blues and coppers, to vigorous skippers, and to heavy-bodied moths, without ruining the specimen.

The use of killing jars has been traditional when collecting insects, and this method remains the most practical for extensive field collecting or when using baits, lights, or traps. Ether, chloroform, and carbon tetrachloride, commonly used in the past, are no longer readily available. This is no loss, since in addition to producing stiff specimens that are difficult to spread, they are either dangerously explosive or can cause chronic toxic effects in humans. Cyanide is used widely by professional entomologists, but it is generally available only to them. Unless used with great care, it can be lethal to humans; a broken bottle can be extremely dangerous. It cannot be recommended for beginners, particularly in situations where it cannot be kept safely away from children.

This leaves ethyl acetate as the best choice, since it is easy to control and quite readily available. It can usually be obtained from biological supply houses or from dealers in chemicals and solvents, listed in the classified telephone directory. It is volatile and flammable and should be stored in a cool place (but *never in a refrigerator*). Breathing concentrated fumes in an enclosed space can cause unconsciousness.

The jar itself should be about twice as deep as it is broad, and the best lid is the type that can be removed or sealed with just a one-quarter turn. Jars of various sizes are convenient, but the diameter of the jar used should be somewhat bigger than the wingspread of the insects being put into it. A circle of cellulose sponge, cut slightly larger than the inside diameter of the jar, should be placed in the bottom and a bit of ethyl acetate poured onto it. Several slightly oversize discs of blotting paper jammed down on top of the sponge help to hold it in place. More ethyl acetate can be dripped onto the blotting paper from time to time as the jar becomes weak. It takes a bit of practice to learn how much to add to keep the concentration strong enough without getting condensation of vapor on the inside of the jar. If this happens, wings will stick on contact and many scales will be lost.

A moth or butterfly put into an adequate killing jar will be knocked out in a few seconds and dead within about ten minutes (with the occasional exception of tiger moths, which at times can have the astonishing ability to revive after hours in a jar). Insects should not be left loose in a jar longer than a few minutes. If you are collecting at bait or at a sheet, it is important to have extra jars, so that several live insects will not be active in the same jar at one time, and so that killed insects can be transferred into another jar for temporary storage. You should not do any prolonged hiking with dead insects piled together in a jar, as the inevitable jostling will cause much wing damage. Whenever it is possible, butterflies, as soon as they are knocked out, should be put into individual envelopes, with the wings folded upward over the back.

STORAGE OF DEAD INSECTS

When traveling you may often lack the time and the equipment to spread specimens the day they are taken, so safe storage must be assured. We usually place specimens in individual glassine envelopes, each labeled with the necessary data for place and date of capture, as well as any other information necessary for the permanent label. Because moths and skippers rarely die with the wings folded upward over the back, it is necessary to arrange them in this position before putting them into the envelopes, and this can be a somewhat tricky undertaking. We find the use of a lepidopterist's "pickle fork" very helpful for this job. It is made from two fairly fine insect pins, thrust through two pieces cut from a rubber band (fig. 31–1) or cemented to opposite sides of a thin stick. The pins are then stuck into the back of the thorax of the dead insect to stabilize it, after which the wings can be folded upward from beneath with the help of some broad-bladed forceps. Stamp forceps are workable, but forceps with curved blades, obtainable from biological supply houses, are much handier (fig. 31–1). With the wings still held up over the back with the forceps, the fork is removed and the insect is put into the envelope. This procedure is also very useful in the field for insects that have died with wings folded downward. With the fork and forceps they can be easily folded upward without handling with the fingers. The fork made with bits of rubber bands can be carried easily in a field pack in a small plastic vial.

Insects stored in envelopes must be protected from shuffling and crushing during transit. Stacking them snugly but not tightly in layers or on edge in rigid boxes, such as plastic sandwich boxes, is ideal. Because the insect bodies are not yet dried out and are hence susceptible to growth of mold within the enclosed boxes, a mold inhibitor must be added. Chlorocresol, available from the supply houses, works very well, but ordinary naphthalene flakes can serve the purpose. If you are collecting in an area with low humidity, you can dry your specimens well before storage and use cardboard boxes. Once mold has started to grow through a specimen, it cannot be salvaged.

Another approach to temporary storage and transport is field-pinning. For this method the insect is pinned through the thorax, as described previously, and then pinned into a wooden or heavy cardboard box with a layer of polyethylene foam glued into the bottom. In a properly

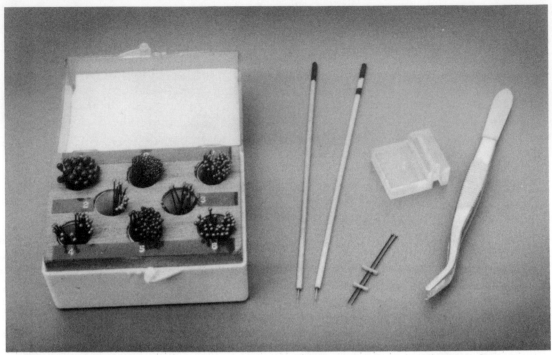

Figure 31–1 Equipment for preparing specimens (*left to right*): insect pins; spreading needles; lepidopterist's "pickle fork"; label block; curved forceps

constructed box the insects can travel safely. The interior of a closed car can serve as an excellent drying oven, but in a humid climate mold can still be a problem.

Insects handled by field-pinning will always have to be relaxed before you can spread them (this will be described shortly), but insects stored in closed plastic boxes with chlorocresol and without drying will often remain soft enough to be spread several weeks after they are taken. For prolonged storage, we find freezing safest and most satisfactory. In the event that storage in the freezer leads to competition with steaks and chops, or even to a domestic crisis, then storage at room temperature, after adequate drying, is perfectly satisfactory. Rigid cardboard or wooden boxes should be used, to allow stacking without crushing the contents. You must take the necessary precautions against damage by "museum pests" (see chapter 32).

RELAXING

The goal of the relaxing process is to restore enough moisture to the dried-out thoracic wing muscles so that the wings can be easily manipulated into the desired position on the spreading board. At the same time, the wings themselves must not be allowed to become wet, or they will stick together and scales will be lost.

A useful container is a broad shallow jar or plastic box with a snugly fitting cover. A layer of sand or sponge in the bottom is moistened with water and covered with a layer or two of blotting paper. Since mold growth is a serious hazard, a few drops of carbolic acid (available in drugstores) should be added as a mold inhibitor.

The specimens to be relaxed must not be allowed to become separated from their collecting data. If all the specimens to be relaxed were collected at the same place and date, they can be removed from their envelopes and laid carefully on the blotting paper, not touching one another. Take care not to damage the brittle antennae. If the specimens are from various places, they are best left within their envelopes, even though this slows the relaxing somewhat. After one to several days, the specimens will be ready to spread: the wings will be loose enough so that, after placing a pin through the thorax, you can easily bend them down below the level of the thorax.

If a specimen is only partly dried out, or is not adequately softened in the relaxing jar, there are a few tricks that are useful. Small, thin-bodied butterflies and moths, such as lycaenids and geometrids, can be relaxed in a few seconds with hot water. Fill a mug with water and put in a cup-heating coil to bring the water to a boil. Then, with the coil turned off (to stop the bubbling), hold the insect by the thorax with narrow bladed forceps and touch the undersurface of the thorax to the surface of the water for ten to thirty seconds. Do not submerge the thorax, or the wings will become wet and damaged. If the specimen is initially soft enough to be pinned safely, do so. Then,

when you touch the thorax to the surface, the water will creep up the pin into the inside and soften the muscles more rapidly.

If the moth or butterfly is too large for this approach, then the injection of a small amount of water is very effective. You will need to persuade a physician friend to give you a small, narrow "tuberculin" syringe with a fine (27- or 30-gauge) hypodermic needle. Insert the needle into the middle of the thorax, and slowly inject a small amount of water. Having a bubble of air present in the syringe makes it possible to control the pressure and inject more smoothly. Leave the needle in place a few minutes while the water soaks into the wing muscles, and the wings will become loose enough to spread. Do not put an insect pin into the thorax before you inject, or the water will immediately escape around the pin.

If an insect is spread when incompletely relaxed, its wings will gradually rise up over the back after it is removed from the spreading board. Small geometrids seem particularly prone to this problem. Special care must also be taken with green moths. Many green pigments in lepidoptera are quite unstable colors, and they can be discolored rapidly by the carbolic acid in the relaxing jar and sometimes by chlorocresol in storage boxes if the boxes are damp. If such moths cannot be spread promptly after capture, they are best stored dry and relaxed by the boiling-water method.

SPREADING

It is said that there is more than one way to skin a cat, and so it is with spreading moths and butterflies. Collectors vary in their preferences as to type of spreading

board and manner of use, but the goal is the same: to end with the spread insects all at the same height on their pins, with their wings in the conventional position already described. Whether you use boards or blocks, and whether you hold the wings in place with pins, paper strips, threads, or combinations thereof is a matter of personal choice. The approach that turns out to be easy, comfortable, and reasonably speedy for you is the right way to do it.

The spreading board itself consists of two parallel pieces of wood, grain running lengthwise, separated by a groove varying in size from about ⅛" for small-bodied insects up to ⅝" for the larger sphinxes and silk moths (fig. 31–2). The width of the side pieces is wider for boards with wider grooves. The board should be a little broader than the wing-spread of the largest insect you intend to spread. A useful assortment is 2⅛" over-all width with ⅛" groove, 2¾" with 3⁄16" groove, 3¼" with ¼" groove, 5" with ⅜" groove, and 6" with ⅝" groove. With these we have been able to spread any North American insects we have taken or reared. If you are working with the smallest micros, special small boards with smaller grooves are necessary.

Spreading boards are not absolutely flat. They are constructed so that the sides slope upward, from the groove to the outer edge, at an angle of 6°. The groove is ⅞" deep and has polyethylene foam or cork in the bottom to hold the pin.

When pinning lepidoptera, it is necessary to use special insect pins (fig. 31–1), obtainable from the supply houses. The pins are 1½" long, stainless steel or enameled black, and have small, unobtrusive nylon heads. They are made in various thicknesses: sizes 2 through 6 are most generally useful (higher numbers are thicker).

Do not use common pins. They are an invitation to trouble. They are too short and thick, the heads are uncomfortable to handle, and after a few years they may corrode and break at the surface of the body.

For pinning, the moth or butterfly must be held from beneath with fingers or forceps, and the pin thrust through the center of the back of the thorax. Care must be taken to position the pin perpendicular to the long axis of the body and to the plane in which the wings will be spread. It is pushed through so that about 7⁄16" remains above the back of the thorax. Take care to avoid rubbing scales from the upper surfaces of the wings while doing this.

Select a spreading board with a groove slightly wider than the body of the insect being spread, and with a width greater than the outspread span of the wings. Push the pin into the groove, perpendicular to the plane of the board, far enough in so that it is firmly seated. The insect's wing bases should be at the level of the edges of the groove, so that they will lie flat when spread. The bug may have to be pushed up or down on the pin a bit to do this leveling.

Strips of smooth paper or similar material (we use acetate tracing film), are used to hold the wings in place. They are secured with glass-headed pins, which are easy on the fingers. Pin the top end of a narrow strip onto each side of the groove. Hold the free end of one strip away from the board, flatten the wings of the left side with the forceps or the side of a smooth needle, and with the left strip hold the wings against the board by keeping tension on the strip with your fingers (fig. 31–2, top left). With a fine point, such as a number 000 insect pin, inserted behind a wing vein, slide the wings forward into the "conventional" position: hind edge of forewing making a right angle with the edge of the groove, and just slightly overlapping the front

Figure 31–2 Spreading technique: (*top left*) inner strips in place, tension being applied to left strip with second and third fingers as left forewing is raised into position; (*top right*) left wings secured, right wings being adjusted; (*bottom left*) outer strips being pinned into place; (*bottom right*) spreading completed, data label made out, spreading date recorded

edge of the hind wing. The wings are held in place by tension on the paper strip, which is then anchored by another glass-headed pin. If the wings tend to slip out of position, they can be pinned in place: use a number 000 insect pin inserted behind a vein, just outside the edge of the paper strip. Repeat the procedure for the right-hand wings, making sure the arrangement is symmetrical (fig. 31–2, top right). Now pin a second pair of strips, wide enough to cover the outer portions of the wings, close to and parallel to the narrow strips. This prevents curling of wing tips and edges (fig. 31–2, bottom left).

There is sometimes a tendency for the body to rotate on the pin during the spreading process. This can be averted by thrusting a heavy pin into the groove just behind the attachment of the hind wing, to the left of the body (fig. 31–2, top left). This pin is removed after all the strips are in place.

Antennae deserve careful attention. They should be spread flat against the board, parallel to the front edge of the forewings, but not touching or overlapping them. Long antennae and feathery ones are best laid against the board at the time the narrow strips are first placed over the wings. Short or filamentous ones, on the other hand, may be dealt with more easily by sliding them under the strips after the wings have been positioned. Experience, and the inevitable destruction of a few fragile antennae, will show which approach works best for you. Well-placed antennae are one of the hallmarks of careful preparation.

Legs will occasionally be caught up on the board beneath a wing. These should be noticed during the spreading process and moved into the groove. Take care not to knock legs off. In many species they bear spurs, spines, and other structures useful for correct identification.

Each specimen should have a data label placed alongside it at the time of spreading. The spreading date should be written on one of the paper strips (fig. 31–2, bottom right). The board is then put into a safe, well ventilated place (out of direct sunlight, which can cause fading), for as long as it takes for the bodies of the insects to dry thoroughly. In medium or low humidity this may take two to three days for a small, thin-bodied moth or butterfly, but up to several weeks for a large sphinx or silk moth. Dryness can be tested by pushing the abdomen lightly from the side with a pin, to see if it has become rigid.

We hang our boards vertically in a tightly constructed, screen-fronted case. The vertical position allows the abdomens to dry out straight, without drooping. The screen keeps out marauding mice and ants, which can be a problem even in the best regulated household.

When the specimens are dry, remove the pins from the paper strips, carefully lift off the strips, then lift the specimen from the board by its pin. Pin it temporarily into a flat piece of corkboard or foam on a wood backing. This is the time to position the data label permanently on the pin. This is best done with the help of a label block: a piece of hardwood or plastic with a $\frac{1}{16}''$ hole bored $\frac{7}{16}''$ deep, into which the pin is thrust through the center of the label. By using such a block (fig. 31–1), all data labels will be at the same height on the pins. If you wish to add a second label for the species name, use a hole $\frac{5}{16}''$ deep. Once the label is in place, the specimen is ready for display or storage.

Many amateur collectors, and all professionals, keep spread lepidoptera pinned in boxes. The advantages are many. Data labels never become separated from the specimens. Both the upper and the undersides of the specimens are accessible for examination, even with a microscope if necessary. It is easy to regroup specimens as more are acquired or identities are clarified. The boxes used are made or specifically adapted for the purpose. All have a pinning surface on the bottom, into which a pin can be thrust easily and held securely. The cork of the past has given way to the ¼″ polyethylene foam of modern technology. The interior depth of the box is 2″. Tight construction to exclude insect pests is important, as are hooks to secure the cover. Uniform size simplifies storage.

One type commonly used is the Schmidt box or its equivalent, with a hinged cover, measuring about 9″ × 13″ × 2½″. Another is the museum drawer, glass-topped with a removable cover, about 17″ × 19″ × 2½″ or 3″. Well-constructed boxes of either type are virtually insect-proof. They can be quite expensive; if you are handy with a bench saw, by all means make your own. Some supply houses carry museum drawer kits of very satisfactory price and quality that you can assemble yourself; you supply the glass.

Some collectors use Riker Mounts, specially constructed glass-topped cardboard boxes about ¼″ thick, which come in many different sizes. Instead of having a pinning bottom, they are filled with a flat mat of cotton or synthetic fibers. Specimens, with labels and pins removed, are laid in position on the cotton and the cover replaced. While these make an attractive display, they have limitations. Removing the pin from a dried specimen calls for a great deal of skill and luck to avoid knocking off antennae or wings or fracturing the body. The legs tend to tangle in the cotton, and

the bodies make depressions, so rearranging specimens is messy. Only the exposed side can be readily viewed, and the data labels can become mixed up. Protection from museum pests can be difficult.

Whatever your choice, avoid the use of makeshifts, such as shoe boxes or cigar boxes. In such containers you will be lucky if you can protect your specimens for more than a year or two.

Thus far nothing has been said about preserving immature stages, which are such fascinating parts of the stories of moths and butterflies. If you are working out the life history of a species whose life cycle has not been previously recorded, specimens should ideally be saved from each of the larval instars, and the pupa as well. Color photography, viewing the larva from above and from the side (and in some instances from beneath, through glass), is very valuable. Actual specimens should also be saved, "pickled" in 70–80 percent alcohol. Sometimes "fixing" solutions of alcohol plus formaldehyde and glacial acetic acid are used for a day or two before alcohol storage. This preserves all the external anatomical features, such as hairs and spines, but does not maintain true colors. An old method, still useful, involves inflating medium or large-size larvae. The soft contents of the larva are squeezed out through the anal opening; the larval skin is then inflated through a hollow quill placed in the opening, and the skin is dried in a diminutive oven over an alcohol lamp. The skins are abnormally stretched out and the colors are faded, but the general shape and external features are well preserved. This technique is fully described in Holland's *Butterfly Book*.

The recently developed technique of freeze-drying gives superb larval specimens, preserved in natural postures on twigs, and undistorted as to color and form—extremely lifelike. Unfortunately, the process calls for a refrigerator run at 20°F, and a very efficient dessicator, vacuum jar, and pump, as well as a number of days' time for each specimen or batch of specimens. The considerable investment in time and dollars makes the process impractical for most amateurs.

Preservation of chrysalids and pupae, on the other hand, is very simple. Photography again is very useful while the insect is in the pupal stage. After the adult has emerged, the empty pupal shell can be pierced with a pin or glued to a pin, a data label attached, and the specimen stored adjacent to that of the emerged adult. Cocoons can be similarly saved, as well as portions of vegetation into which the larvae had bored for feeding or for pupation.

CHAPTER
32

Protection of Collections

A collection of lepidoptera, unlike a collection of coins and stamps, cannot be left hanging on a wall or put away in a closet for years or decades with the expectation that it will remain in unchanged condition. Protection is necessary against many agents of deterioration and destruction.

Most insidious and most devastating are museum pests, particularly carpet beetles or "buffalo bugs." The hairy larvae of these small dermestid beetles thrive on dry animal matter. They eat away within the bodies of your moths and butterflies, perhaps leaving a small pile of dustlike droppings beneath to attract your attention, or perhaps giving little or no clue until what is left of head or abdomen falls to the bottom of the box, leaving one or several wings attached to the pin by the grace of a few bits of sclerotized thorax. The specimen is destroyed, and the beetle larvae, or their offspring, have moved on to destroy adjacent specimens.

Cure of an infested box is difficult, but prevention is less so. Infestation often takes place while the specimens are still on the spreading boards, so it is a good idea, when specimens are first removed to boxes, to put them into a "quarantine box," heavily dosed with crystals of PDB, para-dichlorobenzene. This chemical diffuses throughout the specimens

and kills the pests. Because it is quite volatile, it does not last very long and needs to be replaced often, perhaps every two to three months. For Schmidt boxes, the best PDB container is a small, screen-topped cardboard box pinned securely in place, to prevent loose crystals from rolling about and damaging specimens (fig. 32–1). For drawers, a 1½" length of cardboard tubing, as from a roll of paper towels, glued into one corner, makes a suitable container (fig. 32–2).

PDB has a very low level of toxicity to humans, but it should be used in an area having adequate ventilation. If you are breathing an amount that irritates eyes and nostrils, you are approaching a concentration that is dangerous to some people. This irritation, which should be respected, indicates a need for greatly improved ventilation.

Several short cycles of deep freezing and thawing of an entire drawer or box can effectively decontaminate infested specimens without harming them. A box or drawer found to be infested can also be sterilized by placing a small cup of ethyl acetate inside and keeping the box tightly closed for a day or two.

Once specimens have been disinfected, they can be protected by using repellants. Naphthalene (ordinary moth flakes) is the agent used in most museums because it lasts much longer than

Figure 32–1 Corner of storage box, showing fumigant container

PDB and only needs replenishing every year or two. It does not reliably kill active beetle larvae, but it seems effective in discouraging invasion by the beetles. Its toxicity for people varies and is somewhat higher than PDB. Ventilation of the workplace is the important detail.

Booklice (psocids) are an occasional problem. Infested boxes can be handled by using the freezing or the ethyl acetate treatment, but it is probably impossible to eradicate them from one's house. Sometimes silverfish are a nuisance, but they are more likely to damage labels and the linings of boxes than the insect specimens themselves.

Regardless of the insecticide or repellant used, the more tightly the box or drawer is constructed the better will be the degree and duration of protection. It is for this reason that the use of cigar and shoe boxes is very unsatisfactory. Tight boxes are also good ensurance against wandering ants and rodents.

Humidity is another major threat to collections. In a humid climate, drying requires a longer period, increasing the opportunities for infestation on the spreading boards and favoring mold growth. While this can be reduced in boxes by the use of naphthalene or chlorocresol, these chemicals are not effective on the spreading boards. In addition, spread specimens become softened in conditions of high humidity, resulting in drooping, slipping backward, or clos-

Figure 32–2 Corner of museum drawer, showing cardboard well containing PDB crystals

ing of the wings, the wings in general tending to return to the position in which the insect was stored before spreading. In tropical climates, some collectors find it advantageous to refrain from opening boxes during the rainy season, and to spread specimens only if they can be dried in an artificially heated oven.

An important but subtle threat to collections is light. If kept in the dark, most colors on moths and butterflies show little or no deterioration over hundreds of years, as attested by museum specimens from the eighteenth century. Some of the delicate greens, such as seen in geometrine moths, are exceptions. But specimens in a glass-topped case, particularly if exposed to direct sunlight or ultravio-

let scatter, will fade severely within just a few years. Attractive as they are for wall decorations, butterflies and moths do not hold their colors well under continuous display.

The last and most certain danger to a collection of lepidoptera is deterioration of the collector! Sooner or later you will lose the interest or the ability to care for your collection properly, and it is a rare heir who will be able and willing to do the job right. Sooner rather than later, you should plan to dispose of your specimens, but despite the monetary value of certain species in the commercial market, do not expect to be able to turn your collection into a mountain of cash. You may be lucky enough to find a private individual or a museum interested in purchasing your collection, particularly if it is of a specialized nature or has intensively covered a certain region, but this tends to be the exception. More commonly you may be able to find a museum, university, or science center that will be interested in adding your collection to its holdings or using it for teaching and demonstrations. Since (in the 1980s) each well-prepared, labeled specimen of native moth or butterfly has a value of over one dollar (sometimes more for foreign specimens), you will expect to receive in return a letter acknowledging the total value of your collection as a charitable contribution.

If the proper preparation of specimens, their long-term protection from damage, and ultimate disposition for the benefit of others seem to be responsibilities greater than you wish to undertake, then your collecting should probably not go beyond photographing, rearing, and releasing.

But that is where most of the fun lies!

Appendix A·

FEDERAL LIST OF ENDANGERED SPECIES

Papilio aristodemus ponceanus (Schaus's swallowtail): Florida Keys

Lycaeides idas lotis (Lotis blue): Mendocino County, California

Incisalia mossii bayensis (San Bruno elfin): San Mateo County, California

Icaricia icarioides missionensis (Mission blue): San Mateo County, California

Apodemia mormo langei (Lang's metalmark): Contra Costa County, California

Euphilotes enoptes smithi (Smith's blue): Monterey County, California

Euphilotes battoides allyni (El Segundo blue): Los Angeles County, California

Glaucopsyche lygdamus palosverdesensis (Palos Verdes blue): Los Angeles County, California

Euproserpinus euterpe (Kern primrose sphinx moth): Kern County, California

ORGANIZATIONS OF INTEREST TO LEPIDOPTERISTS

The Lepidopterists' Society, Natural History Museum of Los Angeles County, 900 Exposition Blvd., Los Angeles, California 90007. Worldwide organization, open to all persons interested in any aspect of the study of lepidoptera.

Information on regional organizations, similar in purpose, is available from Lepidopterists' Society members residing in the areas that are of interest. At the time of this writing there are local organizations in Kentucky, Maryland, Massachusetts, Ohio, Ontario, the Pacific Slope, the southeastern United States, and Utah, among others.

The Xerces Society, c/o Entomology Section, Yale Peabody Museum, New Haven, Connecticut 06511. An international organization dedicated to the preservation of the habitats of endangered insects and other arthropods. Membership includes amateur and professional naturalists and conservationists.

COMMERCIAL SUPPLIERS

BioQuip Products, P.O. Box 61, Santa Monica, California 90406. Equipment, books, chemicals.

Carolina Biological Supply Co., Burlington, North Carolina 27215. Equipment, chemicals.

Entomological Reprint Specialists, P.O. Box 77224, Dockweiler Station, Los Angeles, California 90007. Books, current and reprinted.

Ianni Butterfly Enterprises, P.O. Box 81171, Cleveland, Ohio 44181. Insect pins.

Insect Museum Supply, 1021 8th Ave. South, Moorhead, Minnesota 56560. Pins, printed specimen labels.

Ward's Natural Science Establishment, Inc., P.O. Box 92912, Rochester, New York 14603. Equipment, chemicals.

Appendix B·

THE LEPIDOPTERISTS' SOCIETY STATEMENT OF THE COMMITTEE ON COLLECTING POLICY*

PREAMBLE

Our ethical responsibility to assess and preserve natural resources, for the maintenance of biological diversity in perpetuity, and for the increase of knowledge, requires that lepidopterists examine the rationale and practices of collecting Lepidoptera, for the purpose of governing their own activities.

To this end, the following guidelines are outlined, based on these premises:

0.1 Lepidoptera are a renewable natural resource.
0.2 Any interaction with a natural resource should be in a manner not harmful to the perpetuation of that resource.
0.3 The collection of Lepidoptera
    0.31 is a means of introducing children and adults to awareness and study of their natural environment;
    0.32 has an essential role in the elucidation of scientific information, both for its own sake and as a basis from which to develop rational means for protecting the environment, its resources, human health, and the world food supply;
    0.33 is a recreational activity which can generally be pursued in a manner not detrimental to the resource involved.

---

*Published in the NEWS of the Lepidopterists' Society, No. 5, Sept./Oct. 1982. May be reproduced without permission.

GUIDELINES

PURPOSES OF COLLECTING (consistent with the above):

1.1 To create a reference collection for study and appreciation.

1.2 To document regional diversity, frequency, and variability of species, and as voucher material for published records.

1.3 To document faunal representation in environments undergoing or threatened with alteration by man or natural forces.

1.4 To participate in development of regional checklists and institutional reference collections.

1.5 To complement a planned research endeavor.

1.6 To aid in dissemination of educational information.

1.7 To augment understanding of taxonomic and ecologic relationships for medical and economic purposes.

RESTRAINTS AS TO NUMBERS:

2.1 Collection (of adults or of immature stages) should be limited to sampling, not depleting, the population concerned; numbers collected should be consistent with, and not excessive for, the purpose of the collecting.

2.2 When collecting where the extent and/or the fragility of the population is unknown, caution and restraint should be exercised.

COLLECTING METHODS:

3.1 Field collecting should be selective. When consistent with the reasons for the particular collecting, males should be taken in preference to females.

3.2 Bait or light traps should be live-traps and should be visited regularly; released material should be dispersed to reduce predation by birds.

3.3 The use of Malaise or other killing traps should be limited to planned studies.

LIVE MATERIAL:

4.1 Rearing to elucidate life histories and to obtain series of immature stages and adults is to be encouraged, provided that collection of the rearing stock is in keeping with these guidelines.

4.2 Reared material in excess of need should be released, but only in the region where it originated, and in suitable habitat.

Environmental and Legal Considerations:

5.1 Protection of the supporting habitat must be recognized as the *sine qua non* of protection of a species.

5.2 Collecting should be performed in a manner such as to minimize trampling or other damage to the habitat or to specific foodplants.

5.3 Property rights and sensibilities of others must be respected (including those of photographers and butterfly-watchers).

5.4 Regulations relating to publicly controlled areas and to individual species and habitats must be complied with.

5.5 Compliance with agricultural, customs, medical and other regulations should be attained prior to importing live material.

Responsibility for Collected Material:

6.1 All material should be preserved with full data attached, including parentage of immatures when known.

6.2 All material should be protected from physical damage and deterioration, as by light, molds, and museum pests.

6.3 Collections should be made available for examination by qualified researchers.

6.4 Collections or specimens, and their associated written and photographic records, should be willed or offered to the care of an appropriate scientific institution, if the collector lacks space or loses interest, or in anticipation of death.

6.5 Type specimens, especially holotype or allotype, should be deposited in appropriate scientific institutions.

Related Activities of Collectors:

7.1 Collecting should include permanently recorded field notes regarding habitat, conditions, and other pertinent information.

7.2 Recording of observations of behavior and biological interactions should receive as high priority as collecting.

7.3 Photographic records, with full data, are to be encouraged.

7.4 Education of the public regarding collecting and conservation, as reciprocally beneficial activities, should be undertaken whenever possible.

Traffic in Lepidopteran Specimens:

8.1 Collection of specimens for exchange or sale should be performed in accordance with these guidelines.

8.2 Rearing of specimens for exchange or sale should be from stock obtained in a manner consistent with these guidelines, and so documented.

8.3 Mass collecting of Lepidoptera for commercial purposes, and collection or use of specimens for creation of saleable artifacts, are not included among the purposes of the Society.

The foregoing guidelines were developed for the Lepidopterists' Society in 1981–1982, in response to a request of the membership.

The Collecting Policy Committee, which formulated the Guidelines, consisted of H. David Baggett, Lutz, Florida; Keith S. Brown, Jr., Sao Paulo, Brazil; James R. Merritt, Louisville, Kentucky; Lee D. Miller, Sarasota, Florida; Mogens C. Nielsen, Lansing, Michigan; Kenelm W. Philip, Fairbanks, Alaska; Robert M. Pyle, Grays River, Washington; and William D. Winter, Jr., Dedham, Massachusetts (chairman). Consultants included Richard A. Arnold, Berkeley, California; Ian F. B. Common, Canberra, Australia; Charles V. Covell, Jr., Louisville, Kentucky; and the late Robert Silberglied, Barro Colorado Island, Panama.

Glossary ·

Aberration. Variation from the usual or normal configuration.

Aestivation. Dormancy during the warm weather of summer.

Albinism. The state of having a marked absence of normal-colored pigment.

Antennae. The elongated, jointed, paired sensory appendages located above and between the eyes of a moth or butterfly.

Aposematic coloration. Warning colors, usually alternating bands of yellow and black, or red spots on black, to advertise noxiousness or unpalatability.

Brood. The offspring of the females of a single species, from eggs laid at about the same time, and maturing at about the same time.

Chitin. The horny organic material making up the outer, skeletal framework of insects.

Chrysalis. The specialized and often ornate pupa of a butterfly.

Cocoon. The silken, protective envelope inside which a pupa is formed.

Cremaster. A spikelike or hooked structure at the posterior end of a pupa, often used for attachment to a silken anchoring pad.

Cryptic coloration. Coloration designed or patterned to promote concealment.

Deltoids. A group of several subfamilies of small noctuid moths that usually rest with the wings forming a triangular outline.

Diapause. A resting period, during which further development is suspended.

Dimorphism, sexual. The condition of having differences in form or color between sexes of a species.

Frass. Caterpillar droppings, or excrement.

Glycosides, cardiac. Chemical substances, related to digitalis, which cause nausea in small doses and can be lethal in large doses.

Hibernaculum. A structure, crafted by a larva, for protection during hibernation.

Hibernation. Dormancy during the winter.

Imago. The final stage of metamorphosis; the adult moth or butterfly.

Instar. The stage between moults of the larval skin.

Larva. The caterpillar of a moth or butterfly.

Lepidoptera. The order of insects commonly known as moths and butterflies.

Mandibles. The paired chewing structures on a caterpillar's head.

Melanism. The condition of having an excess of dark pigment in scales and hairs.

Metamorphosis. The changes in form occurring during development from egg to adult.

Microlepidoptera. A loosely defined group of families, mostly of small or very small moths, but including some rather primitive families (such as cossids and hepialids) having large moths.

Micropyle. A minute opening in the shell, through which sperm enter the egg.

Ocellus. A small, single-facetted eye.

Osmeterium. A fleshy, extrusible scent gland at the front end of a swallowtail caterpillar.

Ovum. An egg.

Palpi. Paired appendages alongside the mouth.

Parasitoid. An organism living on or within a host's body tissues, consuming them and eventually killing the host.

Phagocyte. A blood cell that consumes and destroys other cells.

Pheromone. A chemical substance that serves as a sex attractant between male and female lepidoptera.

Proboscis. The coiled, hollow tongue through which lepidoptera suck up liquids.

Prolegs. The fleshy abdominal legs of lepidoptera larvae.

Pupa. The stage between larva and adult, during which the adult organs and appendages attain final form.

Sphragis. The waxy concretion applied to the end of the abdomen of the female parnassian by the copulating male.

Spinneret. The organ on the head of a caterpillar from which silk is spun.

Spiracles. Breathing pores located on each side of the abdominal segments.

Stadium. The period between moults in a developing insect.

Bibliography·

FIELD GUIDES

Borror, Donald J. and Richard E. White, *A Field Guide to the Insects*, Boston: Houghton Mifflin Co., 1970. Useful for identification of insect predators and parasitoids.

Covell, Charles V., Jr., *A Field Guide to the Moths of Eastern North America*, Boston: Houghton Mifflin Co., 1984. Color plates and detailed general information for moths east of the great plains.

Ehrlich, Paul R. and Anne H., *How to Know the Butterflies*, Dubuque, Iowa: Wm. C. Brown Co., 1961. Black-and-white illustrated, very useful key to all the butterflies north of Mexico.

Klots, Alexander B., *A Field Guide to the Butterflies of North America, East of the Great Plains*, Boston: Houghton Mifflin Co., 1951. Color plates and detailed general information.

Lutz, Frank E., *Field Book of Insects*, New York: G. P. Putnam's Sons, 1918. Useful for identification of insect predators and parasitoids.

Pyle, Robert M., *The Audubon Society Field Guide to North American Butterflies*, New York: Alfred A. Knopf, 1981. Color illustrations, photographed in the wild; field marks; biological and distribution data.

REFERENCE BOOKS

Dominick, Richard B., et al., *The Moths of America North of Mexico*, Washington, D.C.: The Wedge Entomological Research Foundation, 1971–1985. (The work of many authors, published and continuing to be published in a projected forty or more fascicles: hawkmoths by R. W. Hodges, giant silk and royal moths by D. C. Ferguson, pyralid moths by E. G. Munroe, cosmopterigid moths by Hodges, sack-bearer, apatelodid, tent, and lappet moths by J. G. Franclemont, tussock moths by Franclemont, green geometrids by Ferguson, and most recently, phycitine pyralids by H. M. Neunzig.) The most complete reference work to date for the families listed; outstanding color plates and biological information; found mainly in reference libraries.

Forbes, William M. T., *The Lepidoptera of New York and Neighboring States*, Ithaca, New York: Cornell University, 1923, 1948, 1954, 1960 (four parts). Detailed descriptions, ranges, food plants; almost no illustrations of adult moths; a "backup" resource for advanced amateurs, available in reference libraries (Part 1 reprinted 1969 by Entomological Reprint Specialists, Los Angeles).

Holland, W. J., *The Butterfly Book*, New York: Doubleday and McClure Co., 1898. Color plates and general information on the butterflies of North America north of Mexico; old, but still a primary reference and available in most public libraries.

Holland, W. J., with annotations by A. E. Brower, *The Moth Book*, New York: Dover Publications, Inc., 1968. Color plates and general information on moths of North America north of Mexico. First published in 1903, it is still the only book covering all families of moths of the entire area.

Howe, William H., *The Butterflies of North America*, Garden City, N.Y.: Doubleday and Co., Inc., 1975. Excellent color plates of all the butterflies, extensive biological and general information.

Opler, Paul A., and George O. Krizek, *Butterflies East of the Great Plains*, Baltimore: Johns Hopkins University Press, 1984. Live color photographs, extensive biological and behavioral details, newly compiled distributional maps.

Rockburne, Eric W., and J. Donald Lafontaine, *The Cutworm Moths of Ontario and Quebec*, Ottawa, Ontario: Canada Department of Agriculture Publication 1593, 1976. Color plates and brief descriptions of the noctuid moths (except deltoids) of northeastern Canada and adjacent United States.

Sargent, Theodore D., *Legion of Night: The Underwing Moths*, Amherst, Massachusetts: University of Massachusetts Press, 1976. Color plates and descriptions of the underwings east of the Mississippi River, with extensive chapters on rearing, behavior, and collecting.

Tietz, Harrison M., *An Index to the Described Life Histories, Early Stages, and Hosts of the Macrolepidoptera of the Continental United States and Canada*, Sarasota, Florida: Allyn Museum of Entomology, 1972. A very useful list of larval food plants.

Tyler, Hamilton A., *The Swallowtail Butterflies of North America*, Healdsburg, California: Naturegraph Pub. Inc., 1975. Color-illustrated account of all the swallowtails from the arctic to the southern boundary of Mexico.

REGIONAL WORKS

Emmel, Thomas C. and John F., *The Butterflies of Southern Cali-fornia*, Los Angeles: Natural History Museum of Los Angeles County, 1973. Color plates, excellent drawings of immature stages, distributions.

Ferris, Clifford D., and F. Martin Brown, *Butterflies of the Rocky Mountain States*, Norman, Oklahoma: University of Oklahoma Press, 1981. Color and black-and-white photographs, extensive biological information, detailed distribution maps.

Harris, Lucien, Jr., *Butterflies of Georgia*, Norman, Oklahoma: University of Oklahoma Press, 1972. Color and black-and-white illustrations, descriptions, distributions; useful for southeastern United States.

Kimball, Charles P., *Lepidoptera of Florida*, Gainesville, Florida: Florida Department of Agriculture, 1965. Color and black-and-white illustrations of Florida butterflies and moths, with detailed distributional information.

Morris, Ray F., *Butterflies and Moths of Newfoundland and Labrador*, Hull, Quebec: Agriculture Canada Publication 1691, 1980. Color plates and biological and distributional data for the Province of Newfoundland; useful for Maritimes and northern New England.

Shapiro, Arthur M., *Butterflies of the Delaware Valley*, Philadelphia: American Entomological Society Publication, 1966. A detailed regional treatment, black-and-white drawings.

Shapiro, Arthur M., *Butterflies and Skippers of New York State*, Ithaca, New York: Cornell University, 1974. Descriptions and biology, distribution maps, discussions of geology and habitat.

Tilden, J. W., *Butterflies of the San Francisco Bay Region*, Berkeley: University of California Press, 1965. Color and black-and-white illustrations, descriptions of 122 local species.

GENERAL BACKGROUND

Brewer, Jo, *Wings in the Meadow*, Boston: Houghton Mifflin Co., 1967. A narrative of the life of the monarch butterfly.

Brewer, Jo, and Kjell B. Sandved, *Butterflies*, New York: Harry N. Abrams, Inc., 1976. General discussion of butterflies, their biology, and their role in art and religion (Brewer); striking color photographs (Sandved).

Ford, E. B., *Butterflies*, London: Collins, 1945. An excellent account of the general biology of British butterflies, of interest to students of butterflies everywhere.

Klots, A. B., *The World of Butterflies and Moths*, New York:

McGraw-Hill, Inc., (undated, ca. 1968). A beautifully illustrated general account of the biology of butterflies and moths.

Owen, D. F., *Tropical Butterflies*, Oxford: Clarendon Press, 1971. A very instructive account of butterfly ecology and behavior.

Pyle, Robert M., *Handbook for Butterfly Watchers*, New York: Charles Scribner's Sons, 1984. A general guide to butterfly watching.

FOR THE FOREIGN TRAVELER

D'Abrera, Bernard, *Butterflies of South America*, Ferny Creek, Victoria: Hill House, 1984. Color illustrations and brief data on several hundred representative species; pocket-size.

Higgins, L. D., *A Field Guide to the Butterflies of Britain and Europe*, Boston: Houghton Mifflin Co., 1970. Color plates, descriptions, and distribution maps.

Lewis, H. L., *Butterflies of the World*, Chicago: Follett Pub. Co., 1973. About 7,000 butterflies illustrated in color, brief range data (not a field guide).

Williams, John G., *A Field Guide to the Butterflies of Africa*, Boston: Houghton Mifflin Co., 1971. Color and black-and-white drawings of hundreds of representative species, with ranges and flight periods.

BOTANICAL REFERENCES

Johnson, Charles W., *Bogs of the Northeast*, Hanover, New Hampshire: University Press of New England, 1985. An account of the geology and biology of bogs and fens.

Peterson, Roger Tory, and Margaret McKenny, *A Field Guide to Wild Flowers*, Boston: Houghton Mifflin Co., 1968. Herbaceous plants of northeastern and north central North America.

Petrides, George A., *A Field Guide to Trees and Shrubs*, Boston: Houghton Mifflin Co., 1958. Woody plants of the northeastern and north central United States and southern Canada.

Pohl, Richard W., *How to Know the Grasses*, Dubuque, Iowa: Wm. C. Brown Co., 1953. Identification and distribution of American grasses.

Roth, Charles E., *The Plant Observer's Guidebook*, Englewood Cliffs, New Jersey: Prentice-Hall, Inc., 1984. An excellent practical approach to the study of botany.

Scott, Jane, *Botany in the Field*, Englewood Cliffs, New Jersey: Prentice-Hall, Inc., 1984. An introduction to habitats, plant communities, plant succession.

Index·

Page numbers in italics refer to illustrations. The color insert follows page 114.